NEW YORK STATE MATH A REGENTS COACH

BY
DAVID A. GOLD

EDUCATIONAL DESIGN
EDI 922

ISBN# 0-87694-843-3   EDI 922

TABLE OF CONTENTS

TO THE STUDENT

This book, the **New York State Math A Regents Coach**, will help you prepare for the new Regents A mathematics examination.

The book contains the following sections:

10 units that cover the mathematics on the exam:

- Number and Numeration
- Operations
- Algebraic Modeling
- Geometric Modeling
- Measurement
- Proportional Reasoning
- Relations in Two Variables
- Coordinate Geometry and Locus
- Data Analysis and Probability
- Mathematical Reasoning

Practice Problems at the end of each lesson of each unit

Cumulative Reviews at the end of each unit, covering the contents of that unit

A lesson on test-taking tips

A Practice Test modeled after the actual Regents A Mathematics Examination

Here is how you can use the **New York State Math A Regents Coach** to help you prepare for the test.

1. In each lesson, study the ideas described in the section labeled *Key Concepts You'll Need in this Lesson*. You may want to find these concepts in your textbook and review them before you proceed further.

2. Carefully read each example in the lesson and see how the ideas in the Concepts section are used in working out the example.

3. Try the practice exercises at the end of the lesson. If you have difficulty with them, reread the material in the lesson before trying them again.

4. At the end of each chapter, take the cumulative review. Find the lessons that cover any problems that you had difficulty with and reread those lessons.

5. Finally, take the *Practice Test*, referring to the *Test-Taking Tips*. Here you find useful ideas to help you succeed with all math tests.

Good luck!

LESSON ① THE SET OF RATIONAL NUMBERS

KEY CONCEPTS YOU'LL NEED IN THIS LESSON

1. **Rational numbers** are part of the set of real numbers.

2. Rational numbers are all numbers that can be expressed as the **quotient** or **ratio** of **integers**.

3. Rational numbers include:

    *   counting numbers (1, 2, 3,...)
    *   whole numbers (0, 1, 2, 3,...)
    *   integers (-3, -2, -1, 0, 1, 2, 3,...)
    *   terminating decimals (0.15)
    *   repeating decimals (0.333...)

4. The **square root of any perfect square** is a rational number. For example:

    $$\sqrt{16} = 4, \quad \sqrt{121} = 11, \quad \sqrt{\frac{9}{25}} = \frac{3}{5}$$

    4, 11, and $\frac{3}{5}$ are all rational numbers. 4 and 11 are whole numbers, and $\frac{3}{5}$ is a fraction. $\frac{3}{5}$ can also be expressed as a terminating decimal, 0.6.

    (**Note**: All positive numbers have 2 square roots, one positive, one negative. For example, $\sqrt{9} = 3$, since $3 \times 3 = 9$. But $\sqrt{9}$ is also -3, since $-3 \times -3 = 9$. In this lesson, square roots will refer to the **positive** square root.)

5. Rational numbers can be **compared**.

    On the number line, the **larger** of two real numbers is always to the **right** of the smaller.

    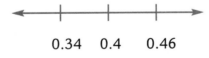

    0.34   0.4   0.46

    *   Since 0.4 is to the right of 0.34, 0.4 > 0.34.
    *   Since 0.4 is to the left of 0.46, 0.4 < 0.46.

    Numbers can be compared by converting them to the same form, either to decimals or to fractions.

6. The **absolute value** of any real number is its distance from 0 on the number line. Since absolute value is a distance, not a direction, it is **always positive** for any number other than 0 itself.

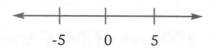

The absolute value of 5 is 5. The absolute value of -5 is also 5.
The symbol for the absolute value of -5 is |-5|.
Since absolute value is always positive, |5| = 5 and |-5| = 5.

1 UNDERSTANDING RATIONAL NUMBERS

EXAMPLE 1   Write $\frac{7}{11}$ as a repeating decimal.

Strategy : **Use Key Concept 2.**

Step 1: Divide the numerator by the denominator: 7 ÷ 11 = 0.63636363...

Step 2: Indicate that the decimal repeats by writing a bar over the repeating part.

Solution: $\frac{7}{11}$ written as a repeating decimal is $0.\overline{63}$.

EXAMPLE 2   Show that the decimal $0.\overline{53}$ is a rational number.

Strategy : **Use Key Concept 2.**

Step 1: Give the decimal a variable name. Let $d = 0.\overline{53}$

Step 2: Multiply the decimal by 100.
$0.\overline{53} \times 100 = 53.535353....$ So, $100d = 53.535353....$

Step 3: Subtract the original decimal.
$53.535353... - 0.535353....$ So, $100d - d = 99d = 53$

Step 4: Divide 53 by 99 and write as a fraction.

Solution: $0.53535353... = \frac{53}{99}$

TIP

$$0.\overline{7} = \frac{7}{9}$$

$$0.\overline{73} = \frac{73}{99}$$

$$0.\overline{738} = \frac{738}{999}$$ and so on. (Look at the denominators.)

EXAMPLE 3

Find the square root of $\frac{16}{49}$.

Strategy : **Use Key Concept 4.**

Step 1: Find the square root of 16: $\sqrt{16} = 4$

Step 2: Find the square root of 49: $\sqrt{49} = 7$

Solution: **The square root of $\frac{16}{49}$, written $\sqrt{\frac{16}{49}}$, is $\frac{4}{7}$.**

2 COMPARING RATIONAL NUMBERS

EXAMPLE 4

Order the following numbers from least to greatest:

$$\frac{1}{\sqrt{25}} \qquad \frac{3}{8} \qquad \sqrt{\frac{1}{4}} \qquad 0.271 \qquad 31\%$$

Strategy : **Use Key Concept 5.**

Step 1: Convert each of the numbers into decimal form.

$$\frac{1}{\sqrt{25}} = \frac{1}{5} = 0.2 \qquad \frac{3}{8} = 0.375 \qquad \sqrt{\frac{1}{4}} = \frac{1}{2} = 0.5 \qquad 31\% = 0.31$$

Step 2: Order the decimal forms of the numbers from least to greatest:

0.2   0.271   0.31   0.375   0.5

Solution: **In order from least to greatest, the given numbers are:**

$$\frac{1}{\sqrt{25}} \qquad 0.271 \qquad 31\% \qquad \frac{3}{8} \qquad \sqrt{\frac{1}{4}}$$

3 ABSOLUTE VALUE

EXAMPLE 5

The absolute value of each of two numbers is 6. What is the distance between the two numbers on the number line?

Strategy : **Use Key Concept 6.**

Step 1: Determine the two numbers that each have an absolute value of 6.

The two numbers are -6 and 6.

Step 2: Find the distance between the two numbers on a number line.

-6 -5 -4 -3 -2 -1 0 1 2 3 4 5 6

Subtract: 6 – (-6) = 12

Solution: **The distance between the two numbers with absolute value of 6 is 12.**

REGENTS MATH PRACTICE

1. Which is another way of writing $\frac{2}{9}$?

   a. 0.2   b. 0.$\overline{2}$ c. 0.29   d. $-\frac{2}{9}$

2. Which is another way of writing 2.45?

   f. $2\frac{4}{5}$ g. 2.4   h. $2\frac{9}{20}$ j. $\frac{14}{5}$

3. Which is another way of writing 0.$\overline{37}$?

   a. 0.38   b. 3.7   c. $\frac{37}{100}$ d. $\frac{37}{99}$

4. The area of a square is 169 square centimeters. What is the length of one side of the square? Explain how you decided.

5. Which of the following numbers can replace x to make a true inequality?

   $\sqrt{225} < x < \sqrt{289}$

   f. 15   g. 16   h. 17   j. 18

6. Which is the only number that cannot be substituted for y to make a true inequality?

   $\sqrt{1} > y > \sqrt{\frac{1}{16}}$

   a. $\frac{7}{8}$ b. 0.$\overline{55}$ c. $\frac{1}{3}$ d. $\frac{1}{5}$

7. Write the numbers in order from least to greatest.

   0.83 $\frac{4}{9}$ $\sqrt{\frac{4}{9}}$ 17% $\frac{3}{\sqrt{9}}$

8. A baseball diamond is a square with an area of 900 yd². What is the length of one side of the diamond in feet? Explain how you decided.

9. Arnoldo and Lissette live along the same road, 16 blocks apart. If they each go home in opposite directions after school, which set of numbers could represent the locations of their homes?

   f. 2, 16   g. -2, 16
   h. -8, 8   j. -16, 16

10. On the number line below, which letter represents the number with the same absolute value as 5?

   a. A   b. B   c. E   d. F

LESSON ②
THE SET OF IRRATIONAL NUMBERS

KEY CONCEPTS YOU'LL NEED IN THIS LESSON

1. **Irrational numbers** are numbers that cannot be written as ratios. All decimals that are both non-repeating and non-terminating are irrational numbers.

    Examples of irrational numbers are 0.15115111511115 . . . and 2.76766766676666 . . .

2. Since irrational numbers are non-repeating, non-terminating decimals, **they are always written as approximations**. No exact rational value can be found for an irrational number.

3. The square root of any positive number that is not a perfect square is an irrational number.

    Examples of irrational numbers are $\sqrt{3}$, which is approximately 1.7320508 . . . and $\sqrt{12}$, which is approximately 3.4641016 . . .

4. The **number** π is an irrational number. For every circle, the ratio of the circumference to the diameter is the non-terminating, non-repeating decimal known as π. A good rational number approximation for π is 3.14.

① RECOGNIZING IRRATIONAL NUMBERS

EXAMPLE 1   **Decide whether the following number is rational or irrational.**
0.676676667 . . .

Strategy :   **Use Key Concept 1.**

Step 1:   First decide whether the decimal is terminating or non-terminating. The three dots at the end of the number indicate that it does NOT terminate.

Step 2:   Decide whether the decimal repeats.
The number consists of a 6 followed by a 7, then two 6's followed by a 7, then three 6's followed by a 7, and so on. It does not repeat.

Solution: **Since the number is a non-terminating, non-repeating decimal, it is an irrational number.**

EXAMPLE 2

Which of the following measures can never be expressed as a rational number?
a. The perimeter of a rectangle
b. The circumference of a circle
c. The volume of a cube
d. The area of a square

Strategy : Use Key Concepts 1, 2, and 4.

Step 1: Examine the situations in order.
a. Since the lengths of the sides of a rectangle may be rational numbers, an exact value can be found.
b. Since the circumference of a circle is found using the formula $C = \pi d$, and π is irrational, no exact rational value can be found for a circle's circumference.
c. The length of the edge of a cube may be a rational number, so an exact value for a cube's volume is possible.
d. The length of a square's side may be rational, so an exact area is possible.

Solution: **No exact rational value can be found for the circumference of a circle, answer choice b.**

EXAMPLE 3

A square has an area of 75 ft². Is the length of a side of the square a rational or irrational number?

Strategy : Use Key Concepts 2 and 3.

Step 1: Recall the area formula for a square: $A = s^2$ where s is the length of a side.

Step 2: Use the area formula to find the length of a side:
$A = 75$, so $75 = s^2$ and $\sqrt{75} = s$

Step 3: Decide whether $\sqrt{75}$ is rational or irrational.
Since 75 is not a perfect square, $\sqrt{75}$ must be irrational.

Solution: **The length of a side of the square is irrational.**

EXAMPLE 4

If the radius of a circle is 9 cm, between which two whole numbers is the area?

Strategy : Use Key Concept 4.

Step 1: Recall the area formula for a circle: $A = \pi r^2$

Step 2: Apply the formula, using the given radius and 3.14 for π.
$A = \pi r^2 \qquad A \approx 3.14 \times 9^2 \qquad A \approx 3.14 \times 81 \approx 254.34$

Solution: **The area of the circle is between 254 cm² and 255 cm².**

REGENTS MATH PRACTICE

1. Which number or numbers are irrational?
   a. 1.121212…
   b. 0.$\overline{45}$
   c. $\sqrt{35}$
   d. $\sqrt{200}$

2. Which number or numbers are rational?
   f. 0   g. -13   h. 4.59   j. $\sqrt{1}$

3. Which set of numbers is ordered correctly from least to greatest?
   a. 2, $\sqrt{3}$, 4
   b. $\sqrt{2}$, 3, $\sqrt{4}$
   c. $\sqrt{2}$, $\sqrt{3}$, 2
   d. 2, $\sqrt{3}$, $\sqrt{4}$

4. Which of the following measures will always be approximate? Explain how you decided.
   f. The area of a trapezoid
   g. The volume of a square pyramid
   h. The perimeter of a hexagon
   j. The volume of a sphere

5. Which is the best estimate for the length of a side of a square whose area is 60 in.²?
   a. $\sqrt{60}$ b. 6   c. 7.7   d. 15

6. Between which two consecutive integers is the value of $\sqrt{300}$?
   f. 14 and 15   g. 15 and 16
   h. 16 and 17   j. 17 and 18

7. The length of a side of a square is $\sqrt{45}$. What is the area of the square? Explain your answer.
   a. 6.7082039…   b. 45
   c. 90   d. 2025

8. Use the fact that the sum of a rational number and an irrational number is an irrational number. Which of the following are irrational?
   f. $\sqrt{25}$ + $\sqrt{100}$ g. $\sqrt{50}$ + $\sqrt{36}$
   h. π + 4   j. $\sqrt{9}$ + π

9. Which of the following statements must be estimates? Explain your answer.
   a. The area of a parallelogram is calculated to be 96 in².
   b. The circumference of a circle is calculated to be 20 cm.
   c. The volume of the cube is calculated to be 64 cm³.
   d. The area of a circle is calculated to be 50 in.²

10. To the nearest whole number, what is the length of a side of a square whose area is 160 m²?
   f. 12 m   g. 12.6 m
   h. 13 m   j. 16 m

LESSON ③ PROPERTIES OF REAL NUMBERS

KEY CONCEPTS YOU'LL NEED IN THIS LESSON

1. **Closure**: A set of numbers is said to be closed under an operation if that operation always results in exactly one number that is a member of the set.

    Example: The set of real numbers is closed under addition, since any addition of two real numbers results in exactly one real number: $6 + 9 = 15$, and only 15.

    But the set of odd counting numbers (1, 3, 5, ...) is **not** closed under the operation of addition or subtraction since these operations do not have to result in an odd counting number: $3 + 7 = 10$ (an even number) and $9 - 5 = 4$ (an even number).

2. **Commutative Property**: Addition and multiplication of real numbers are commutative. The order in which the operations are performed does not affect the result.

    Examples: $3 + 9 = 9 + 3$, $x + y = y + x$ $5(2) = 2(5)$, $xy = yx$

3. **Associative Property**: Addition and multiplication of real numbers are associative. The way in which the numbers are grouped does not affect the outcome.

    Examples: $5 + (6 + 1) = (5 + 6) + 1$ $a + (b + c) = (a + b) + c$
    $4 \times (3 \times 7) = (4 \times 3) \times 7$ $a \times (b \times c) = (a \times b) \times c$

4. **Distributive Property**: For the set of real numbers, multiplication is distributive over addition.

    Examples: $3(6 + 4) = 3(6) + 3(4)$ $a(b + c) = ab + ac$

5. **Inverse Elements**: If two real numbers have a **sum of 0**, they are **additive inverses**. If two real numbers have a **product of 1**, they are **multiplicative inverses**.

    Examples of additive inverses: $6 + (-6) = 0$, so 6 and -6 are additive inverses. In general, a and $-a$ are additive inverses.
    Examples of multiplicative inverses: $3(\frac{1}{3}) = 1$, so 3 and $\frac{1}{3}$ are multiplicative inverses. In general, a and $\frac{1}{a}$ are multiplicative inverses if $a \neq 0$.

6. **Identity Elements**: For real numbers, 0 is the **identity element for addition**. This means that if you add 0 to a number, you get the identical number as an answer. For real numbers, 1 is the **identity element for multiplication**.

    Examples: $4 + 0 = 4$, $0 + 4 = 4$, $a + 0 = a$;
    $8 \times 1 = 8$, $1 \times 8 = 8$, $a \times 1 = a$

1 PROPERTIES

EXAMPLE 1

Can you give examples to show that the set of odd counting numbers (1, 3, 5, ...) is closed: squaring? under division? If not, give a counterexample to demonstrate.

Strategy: **Use Key Concept 1.**

Step 1: *Squaring*: Try several examples to see whether a pattern appears to develop.

$3^2 = 9,$ $5^2 = 25,$ $7^2 = 49,$ $11^2 = 121,$ $13^2 = 169,...$

It appears that the square of every odd counting number is also odd, and that it is a unique member of the set of odd counting numbers.

Step 2: *Division*: Again, try several examples.

$25 \div 5 = 5,$ $45 \div 15 = 3$ So far, they are all odd numbers.

But, $9 \div 5 \neq$ a member of the set of odd counting numbers. When you divide an odd number by an odd number, the answer is not part of the set of odd counting numbers at all.

Solution: **From the examples, it appears that the set of odd counting numbers is closed under squaring. However, it can be shown by a counterexample that the set of odd counting numbers is not closed under division.**

EXAMPLE 2 **Use the following figure:**

3 cm

12 cm   6 cm

Which property of real numbers would you use to find the area of the whole figure? Write two expressions for the area.

Strategy: **Use Key Concepts 2, 3, and 4.**

Step 1: Recall the Commutative, Associative, and Distributive Properties.
The *Commutative* states that the order in which addition or multiplication is performed does not affect the result.
The *Associative* states that for addition or multiplication, the grouping does not affect the result.
The *Distributive* allows addition to be stated as multiplication.

| Step 2: | Decide which property applies to the problem. |
| Solution: | **The Distributive Property applies to the problem. The expressions 3(12 + 6) and 3(12) + 3(6) can both be used to find the area.** |

EXAMPLE 3

For which value of w does the expression $w - 1$ have no multiplicative inverse?

Strategy:	**Use Key Concept 5.**
Step 1:	Recall the meaning of multiplicative inverse: For any real number, $a\left(\frac{1}{a}\right) = 1$, if $a \neq 0$.
Step 2:	Think of a value for w that will give the expression $w - 1$ a value of 0. When $w = 1$, the expression $w - 1 = 0$.
Solution:	**When $w = 1$, the expression $w - 1$ will have no multiplicative inverse.**

EXAMPLE 4

If $r + s = s$, what is the value of $s - r$?

Strategy:	**Use Key Concept 6.**
Step 1:	Recall the identity element for addition: $a + 0 = a$.
Step 2:	Apply the identity element to the equation $r + s = s$. In this equation, r must be 0.
Step 3:	Substitute 0 for r in the expression $s - r$.
Solution:	**If $r + s = s$, then $s - r = s$.**

REGENTS MATH PRACTICE

In problems 1–4, write Yes or No. If the answer is No, give a counterexample.

1. Is the set (even counting numbers) closed under addition?

2. Is the set (counting numbers that are multiples of 4) closed under multiplication?

3. Is the set (counting numbers that are multiples of 5) closed under subtraction?

4. Is the set (counting numbers that are multiples of 3) closed under division?

5.

   Which expression would you use to find the area of the entire figure shown above?
   a. 2(14) + 8   b. 8(2) + 14
   c. 2(14 × 8)   d. 2(14 + 8)

6. Which expression is a correct application of the Distributive Property?
   f. 7(x + 4) = 7x + 4
   g. 8 + 5m = (8 + 5)m
   h. (a + 3)b = ab + 3b
   j. 9m + 2 = 9(m + 2)

In problems 7 and 8, name the property illustrated.

7. Three students each carried 4 books from the book supply room. Each student made 2 trips. In another class, 3 trips were made by 4 students, each carrying 2 books per trip. Each group of students carried the same total number of books.

8. In a card game, each of 5 friends was dealt 9 cards. In another game, each of 9 friends was dealt 5 cards. In each case, the same number of cards were dealt.

9. For what value of x will the expression $2x - 4$ have no multiplicative inverse?

10. If $x + y = y$, what is the value of xy? Explain your answer.

UNIT ❶ REVIEW

1. Each of the following represents the area of a square.
   Which square does not have a
   side length that is a rational
   number? Explain your choice.
   a. 196 cm²
   b. 225 in.²
   c. 289 mm²
   d. 321 cm²

2. Which value of x makes the following inequality true?
   $\sqrt{x} < 2(\sqrt{x}) < x$
   f. 0   g. 1   h. 4   j. 16

3. What is the fraction equivalent
   of 0.89? How does your explanation prove that the decimal is
   rational?

4. Order these numbers from least
   to greatest.
   $\frac{5}{9}$ $\sqrt{\frac{16}{36}}$ 40%   0.44 $\frac{\sqrt{4}}{7}$

5. Which can be the absolute
   value of each of two numbers
   whose product is -36?
   a. 6 and 6   b. -4 and -9
   c. -4 and 9   d. -6 and 6

6. Natasha told her friend that by
   using a radius of 3 in., she had
   constructed a circle whose area
   was exactly 28 in.² What was
   wrong with Natasha's reasoning?

7. Which set is correctly ordered
   from least to greatest?
   f. $\sqrt{5}$, 2, 3
   g. 2, $\sqrt{5}$, $\sqrt{7}$
   h. 3, $\sqrt{7}$, 4
   j. 3, $\sqrt{5}$, $\sqrt{7}$

8. A square has an area of
   200 cm². Which of the following
   statements is true?
   a. The length of a side is a
      rational number between
      14 and 15.
   b. The length of a side is an
      irrational number between
      14 and 15.
   c. The length of a side is $\sqrt{200}$
      and is a rational number.
   d. The length of a side is an
      irrational number between
      13 and 14.

9. Under which of the following
   operations is the set (counting
   numbers that are multiples of
   4) closed?
   f. addition and subtraction
   g. addition and division
   h. subtraction and multiplica-
      tion
   j. addition and multiplication

10. If $x - y = x$, what is the value of
    xy? Explain your answer.

LESSON ④
OPERATIONS ON SIGNED NUMBERS

KEY CONCEPTS YOU'LL NEED IN THIS LESSON

1. The **absolute value** of a number is its distance from 0 on the number line. Absolute value is positive for every number other than 0.

    |5| = 5 |-5| = 5 |0| = 0

2. To **add** signed numbers:

    • With the **same** signs: Add absolute values, keep the sign.

    • With **different** signs: Subtract absolute values, use the sign of the number with the greater absolute value.

3. To **subtract** signed numbers:

    Change the sign of the second number. Then solve as an addition problem of signed numbers.

4. To **multiply** or **divide** signed numbers:

    • If the signs are the same, the result is positive.

    • If the signs are different, the result is negative.

---

① **ADDITION AND SUBTRACTION**

EXAMPLE 1	**Find the sum of (+6) and (-8).**
Strategy:	**Use Key Concepts 1 and 2.**
Step 1:	Write the absolute value of each number: |+6| = 6, |-8| = 8
Step 2:	Subtract absolute values: 8 – 6 = 2
Step 3:	Use the sign of the number with the greater absolute value. 8 > 6, so use a negative sign.
Solution:	**The sum of (+6) and (-8) is -2.**

EXAMPLE 2	Subtract: (-4) – (-7)
Strategy:	Use Key Concepts 1 and 3, and then 2.
Step 1:	Change the sign of the second number: change (-7) to 7.
Step 2:	Add (-4) + (+7) = 3 (Remember to use the procedure for adding numbers with different signs.)
Solution:	(-4) – (-7) = 3

2 MULTIPLICATION AND DIVISION

EXAMPLE 3	Find the product: (-5)(-4)
Strategy:	Use Key Concepts 1 and 4.
Step 1:	Multiply absolute values: |-5| = 5, |-4| = 4 5 × 4 = 20
Step 2:	Use a positive sign, since each factor has the same sign.
Solution:	(-5)(-4) = 20

EXAMPLE 4	Divide: (-18) ÷ (+9)
Strategy:	Use Key Concepts 1 and 4.
Step 1:	Find the quotient of the absolute values: |-18| = 18, |+9| = 9 18 ÷ 9 = 2
Step 2:	Use a negative sign, since (-18) and (+9) have different signs.
Solution:	(-18) ÷ (+9) = -2

REGENTS MATH PRACTICE

In questions 1–4, choose the value that completes the equation.

1. $|-3| + |-3| = ?$
   a. -6   b. -3   c. 0   d. 6

2. $\dfrac{?}{|-2|} = 8$
   f. -4   g. -16   h. 16   j. 4

3. $|10| - |-7| = ?$
   a. 17   b. 3   c. -3   d. -17

4. $|-6| \times |-3| = ?$
   f. 18   g. 2   h. -2   j. -18

In questions 5–10, find the value of the given expression.

5. $(-8) - (+7) = $ _____

6. $(-2)^2 = $ _____

7. $0 \div (-3) = $ _____

8. $(-35) \div (-7) = $ _____

9. $(-3)(+13) = $ _____

10. $(-50) \div \left(\dfrac{-1}{2}\right) = $ _____

LESSON ⑤
EVALUATING ALGEBRAIC EXPRESSIONS AND FORMULAS

KEY CONCEPTS YOU'LL NEED IN THIS LESSON

1. The **order of operations** for calculations is:
   - Work inside parentheses first, following the next 3 steps as they apply.
   - Simplify exponents.
   - Do all multiplications and divisions reading from left to right.
   - Do all additions and subtractions reading from left to right.

2. When simplifying a fraction, simplify the numerator. Then simplify the denominator. Finally, divide.

3. An exponent refers only to the term directly to its left.

   So, $4(5)^2$ means $4 \times 25 = 100$
   and $6(2m)^2$ means $6(2m)(2m) = 6 \times 2 \times 2 \times m \times m = 24m^2$
   but $6(2)(m)^2$ means $6(2)(m)(m) = 6 \times 2 \times m \times m = 12m^2$

4. To evaluate an algebraic expression or formula:
   - Substitute the given values for each variable, then
   - Simplify the numerical expression, following the order of operations.

5. A formula expresses the relationship between two or more variables. When there is only one unknown value in the formula, that value can be found.

---

① NUMERICAL AND ALGEBRAIC EXPRESSIONS

EXAMPLE 1 **Simplify the expression:** $\dfrac{100 - 2(9 + 4^2)}{2(5)^2}$

Strategy: **Use Key Concepts 1, 2, and 3.**

Step 1: Simplify the numerator according to the order of operations.
$100 - 2(9 + 4^2) \rightarrow 100 - 2(9 + 16) \rightarrow 100 - 2(25) \rightarrow 100 - 50 = 50$

Step 2: Simplify the denominator, again following the order of operations.
$2(5^2) \rightarrow 2 \times 25 = 50$

Step 3: Divide the numerator by the denominator.
$\dfrac{50}{50} = 1$

Solution: **The value of the expression is 1.**

EXAMPLE 2   Evaluate the expression $2mn^2 - 3m$ when $m = 2$ and $n = -3$.

Strategy: Use Key Concepts 1, 3, and 4.

Step 1:   Substitute the values for m and n into the expression.
$2mn^2 - 3m$ → $2(2)(-3)^2 - 3(2)$

Step 2:   Simplify the expression, following the order of operations.
$2(2)(-3)^2 - 3(2)$ → $2(2)(9) - 3(2)$ → $36 - 6 = 30$
When $m = 2$ and $n = -3$, the expression $2mn^2 - 3m = 30$.

Solution:

---

2   WORKING WITH FORMULAS

EXAMPLE 3   **The classroom pictured below has two carpeted sections as shown.**

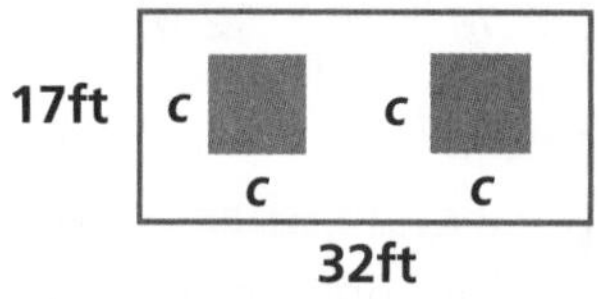

17ft

32ft

a. Write a formula for the area of the floor that is not carpeted.
b. Find the area of the uncarpeted section when $c = 9$.

Strategy: Use Key Concepts 1, 3, 4, and 5.

Step 1:   Use the given information to write the formula:
Area of uncarpeted section = Area of room – Area of carpeted sections
A $=$ $32(17)$ $-$ $2(c)^2$

Step 2:   Evaluate the expression on the right side of the formula.
$32(17) - 2(c)^2$ when $c = 9$.
$32(17) - 2(9)^2$ → $32(17) - 2(81)$ → $544 - 162 = 382$

Solution: **a. The formula for the area of the uncarpeted part is**
    $A = 32(17) - 2c^2$
b. When $c = 9$, the area of the uncarpeted part is 382 ft².

REGENTS MATH PRACTICE

In questions 1–3, simplify the expression.

1. $3^2 - 2(8 - 4 \times 3)$ _____

2. $40 + 7(4) \div 2 - 3$ _____

3. $\dfrac{16 - 3^2 + 4(5)}{5 + (-2)^2}$ _____

In questions 4–6, evaluate the expression when x = -2, y = 3, and z = 6.

4. $\dfrac{xy}{2} - \dfrac{z}{3}$ _____

5. $\dfrac{4z - 3y}{x}$ _____

6. $12z + 3y - 4x$ _____

In questions 7–10, write a formula to find A, the area of the picture frame. Then find the area for the given values of the variables.

7. 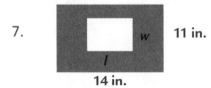 11 in.

14 in.

Find the area of the picture frame when *l* = 8 in. and *w* = 5 in.

8. Find the area of the picture frame when *l* = 20, *w* = 10, and *a* = 4.

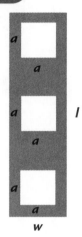

9.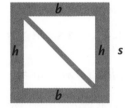

Find the area of the square picture frame when *s* = 12, *b* = 8, and *h* = 8.

10.

Find the area of the picture frame when *l* = 18, *w* = 12, *b* = 6, and *h* = 6.

LESSON 6
MONOMIAL AND POLYNOMIAL OPERATIONS: ADDITION AND SUBTRACTION

KEY CONCEPTS YOU'LL NEED IN THIS LESSON

1. A **term** or **monomial** may contain a number, a variable, or both.
   - The variable may be raised to a power other than 1.
   - Parts of terms are connected by multiplication.
   - Terms are separated by addition or subtraction.

   Examples of terms: 9, $3x$, $2m^3$, $5x^3y^2$

2. **Like terms** contain the same variable or variables, each identical variable raised to the same power.

   Examples of like terms: $4a$ and $7a$, a^3 and $2a^3$, $3m^2n$ and $5m^2n$

3. Like terms may be **combined** by addition or subtraction. Use the distributive property.

   For example: $5m^3 + 2m^3 = (5 + 2)m^3 = 7m^3$ $10r^3s - 4r^3s = (10 - 4)r^3s = 6r^3s$

4. When two or more monomials are **not like terms**, they **cannot be combined** by addition or subtraction. Their sum or difference must be written as a polynomial.

   For example: In the polynomial $8x^2 + 2y$, the terms cannot be combined by addition or subtraction.

---

1 ADDITION

EXAMPLE 1

A triangle has the following side lengths: $3x + 4$, $2x$, and $5x - 3$. Express the perimeter of the triangle as a polynomial.

Strategy: Use Key Concepts 1, 2, and 3.

Step 1: Write a formula for the perimeter of a triangle.
$P = a + b + c$ where a, b, and c are the side lengths.

Step 2: Substitute the given lengths in the formula.
$P = 3x + 4 + 2x + 5x - 3$

Step 3: Arrange the terms so that like terms are together.
$P = 3x + 2x + 5x + 4 - 3$

Step 4: Use the Distributive Property.
$P = (3 + 2 + 5)x + 4 - 3 = 10x + 1$

Solution: **The perimeter of the triangle is $10x + 1$.**

EXAMPLE 2

Two sweaters cost $7x + 2$ dollars and $6y - 5$ dollars. What is their combined cost?

Strategy: Use Key Concept 4.

Step 1: Write an algebraic sentence that describes the information in the problem.
Cost = $(7x + 2) + (6y - 5)$

Step 2: Arrange the terms so that like terms are together. In this case, only the numerals can be combined.
$C = 7x + 6y + 2 - 5$

Step 3: Write the polynomial that describes the total cost: $C = 7x + 6y - 3$

Solution: The two sweaters cost a total of $7x + 6y - 3$ dollars.

2 SUBTRACTION

EXAMPLE 3

In an experiment, a golf ball bounced to a height of $2x^2 - 5x - 1$ feet when dropped from a building. A rubber ball bounced $x^2 - 8x + 2$ feet from the same building. How many feet higher did the golf ball bounce?

Strategy: Use Key Concepts 2 and 3.

Step 1: Write an algebraic expression that describes the problem.

$$2x^2 - 5x + 1$$
$$- \ (x^2 - 8x + 2)$$

Step 2: Subtract to find the difference in bounce heights. Remember, to subtract signed numbers, change the sign of **each term** in the second polynomial. Then it can be treated as an addition.

$$\begin{array}{ll} 2x^2 - 5x + 1 & \qquad 2x^2 - 5x + 1 \\ - \ (x^2 - 8x + 2) & \qquad - \ x^2 + 8x - 2 \\ \hline & \qquad x^2 + 3x - 1 \end{array}$$

Solution: The golf ball bounced $x^2 + 3x - 1$ feet higher.

EXAMPLE 4 | Simplify the following expression:
$(7a^3 - 4a) - (2b + 3)$

Strategy: Use Key Concept 4.

Step 1: Examine the expression. There are no like terms. Therefore, no terms can be combined.

Solution: The expression is already in simplest form.

REGENTS MATH PRACTICE

In questions 1–6, simplify the expression if possible. If not possible, explain why.

1. $3x + 8y - 6x + 4y$

2. $(m^2n^5 - 2mn) - (-m^2n^5 + 2mn)$

3. $(y^2 - 6y + 3) + (-3y - 4)$

4. $15 - (-2a + 5b + 9)$

5. $(12a^2 + 5a^2b) - (9ab + 4b^2)$

6. $(8x^2 + 4x - 5) + (-6x^2 - 7x + 3)$

7. A television screen is in the shape of a rectangle. If the length is $6x + 4$ inches and the width is $5x - 1$ inches, how much greater is the length than the width?

8. The length of a side of a rhombus is $3m^3 - 4$. What is its perimeter?

9. In a right triangle, the length of the hypotenuse is $7a - 1$. The length of each leg is $3a + 5$. What is the perimeter of the triangle?

10. A truck weighs $(15a + 17)$ pounds. How many pounds of cargo can be added to the truck to bring it to its maximum legal weight of $(21a - 5)$ pounds?

LESSON 7
MONOMIAL AND POLYNOMIAL OPERATIONS: MULTIPLICATION AND DIVISION

KEY CONCEPTS YOU'LL NEED IN THIS LESSON

1. To **multiply powers** with the same base, **add the exponents.**
$a^2 \cdot a^5 = a \cdot a \cdot a \cdot a \cdot a \cdot a \cdot a = a^7$, so $a^2 \cdot a^5 = a^{2+5} = a^7$

2. To take **a power of a power, multiply the exponents.**
$(m^2)^3 = m^2 \cdot m^2 \cdot m^2 = m^6$, so $(m^2)^3 = m^{2 \cdot 3} = m^6$

3. Any two monomials can be multiplied. Multiply numerical coefficients and multiply like variables.
$(2x^2)(5x^3y) = 10x^5y$

4. To **multiply a polynomial by a monomial**, use the Distributive Property.
$3y(x^2y + 2y^3) = 3x^2y^2 + 6y^4$

5. To **multiply two polynomials**, treat the problem as though it were arithmetic.

$$
\begin{array}{r}
(3x - 2) \\
\times (-2x + 3) \\
\hline
-6x^2 + \underline{4x + 9x} - 6 \\
13x
\end{array}
$$

Think, for example:
$$
\begin{array}{r}
35 \rightarrow 30 + 5 \\
\times\ 19 \rightarrow\ \underline{10 + 9} \\
300 + 50 + 270 + 45 = 665
\end{array}
$$

6. To **divide powers** with the same base, **subtract** the exponents.
$b^6 \div b^4 = \dfrac{b \cdot b \cdot b \cdot b \cdot b \cdot b}{b \cdot b \cdot b \cdot b} = b \cdot b = b^2$, so $b^6 \div b^4 = b^{6-4} = b^2$

7. To **divide a polynomial by a monomial**, divide **each term** of the polynomial.
$\dfrac{6m^2n + 2mn - 2n}{2n} = 3m^2 + m - 1$

1 MULTIPLICATION

EXAMPLE 1   The length of the side of a square is $5x^2$.
a. Express the perimeter of the square.
b. Express the area of the square.
c. Find each measure when $x = 2$.

Strategy: **Use Key Concepts 1, 2, and 3.**

Step 1: Find the perimeter. Recall that the perimeter of a square is $4s$ where s is the length of a side.
Perimeter = $4(5x^2) = 20x^2$

Step 2: Find the area. Recall that the area of a square is s^2 where s is the length of a side.
Area = $(5x^2)^2 = 5x^2(5x^2) = 5 \cdot 5 \cdot x^2 \cdot x^2 = 25x^4$

Step 3: Evaluate each expression when $x = 2$.
Perimeter: $20x^2 = 20(2)^2 = 20(4) = 80$
Area: $25x^4 = 25(2)^4 = 25(16) = 400$

Solution: **a. The perimeter is $20x^2$ units.**
b. The area is $25x^4$ units².
c. When $x = 2$, the side is 20 units, the perimeter is 80 units, and the area is 400 units².

EXAMPLE 2 **A car is traveling a constant rate of $a^4 - 5ab$ miles per hour.**
a. Express the distance it would travel in ab hours.
b. Find the distance traveled in ab hours when $a = 3$ and $b = 2$.

Strategy: **Use Key Concepts 1, 2, and 4.**

Step 1: Express the distance traveled in ab hours.
Write a sentence to represent the information in the problem:
Distance = rate $\times$ time = $(a^4 - 5ab)ab = ab(a^4 - 5ab)$

Step 2: Multiply the expressions. Use the Distributive Property.
$ab(a^4 - 5ab) = a^5b - 5a^2b^2$

Step 3: Evaluate $a^5b - 5a^2b^2$ when $a = 3$ and $b = 2$.
$$a^5b - 5a^2b^2 = (3^5)2 - 5(3^2)(2^2)$$
$$= (243)2 - 5(9)(4)$$
$$= 486 - 180$$
$$= 306 \text{ miles}$$

Solution: **a. The total distance is $a^5b - 5a^2b^2$.**
b. When $a = 3$ and $b = 2$, the total distance is 306 miles.

EXAMPLE 3

A carton weighs $y - 2$ pounds. If $y + 7$ cartons are loaded onto a truck, what is the total weight that the truck must carry?

Strategy: Use Key Concepts 1, 2, and 5.

Step 1: Write a multiplication sentence that describes the information in the problem.

$$(y - 2)$$
$$\times (y + 7)$$

Step 2: Multiply $y - 2$ by y. Then multiply $y - 2$ by 7. Add the two partial products.

$$(y - 2)$$
$$\underline{\times (y + 7)}$$
$$y^2 - 2y \qquad \text{partial product of } y \text{ and } y - 2$$
$$\underline{+ \ 7y - 14} \qquad \text{partial product of 7 and } y - 2$$
$$y^2 + 5y - 14$$

Solution: The truck must carry $y^2 + 5y - 14$ pounds.

---

2 DIVISION

EXAMPLE 4

The area of a rectangle is $4x^3 - 2x^2 + 8x$. If the width of the rectangle is $2x$, find the length.

Strategy: Use Key Concepts 6 and 7.

Step 1: Recall the area formula for a rectangle: $A = lw$. So, $l = \frac{A}{w}$. Write a sentence that describes the problem.

$$l = \frac{4x^3 - 2x^2 + 8x}{2x}$$

Step 2: Divide the numerator by the denominator.

$$\frac{4x^3 - 2x^2 + 8x}{2x} = 2x^2 - x + 4$$

Solution: The length of the rectangle is $2x^2 - x + 4$ units.

REGENTS MATH PRACTICE

In questions 1–5, find the product or quotient.

1. $(6e^3)(-4e^4)$

2. $3mn(2m - 3n^2)$

3. $(4x - 2)(2x + 5)$

4. $\dfrac{35a^4b^5}{7a^2b}$

5. $\dfrac{12x^2 - 8x}{-2x}$

6. A tank holds $(x^2 + 3x)$ gallons of water. Write the capacity of the tank in quarts.

7. A total of $(p^3 - 3q + r)$ tiles is needed to cover the floor of a room. How many tiles are needed for $2p$ rooms?

8. During one week, a movie theater sold an average of $(30r + 5)$ tickets per show. There were $(4r - 1)$ shows. How many tickets were sold during the week?

9. There are $(21x^2 - 14x)$ days until the end of the year. Write the number of weeks until the end of the year.

10. A store sold $(12y^2 + 18y)$ pounds of apples in $3y$ days. What was the average number of apples sold per day?

LESSON ⑧
EXPONENTS AND SCIENTIFIC NOTATION

KEY CONCEPTS YOU'LL NEED IN THIS LESSON

1. **Zero** can be used as an exponent.

   Since $x^2 \div x^2 = x^{2-2} = x^0$ and $\dfrac{x^2}{x^2} = \dfrac{x \cdot x}{x \cdot x} = 1$,
   it follows that $x^0 = 1$.

2. Exponents can be **negative**.

   Since $x^2 \div x^5 = \dfrac{x \cdot x}{x \cdot x \cdot x \cdot x \cdot x} = \dfrac{1}{x^3}$ and $x^2 \div x^5 = x^{2-5} = x^{-3}$,

   it follows that $x^{-3} = \dfrac{1}{x^3}$.

3. Very large and very small positive numbers can be written in **scientific notation**.
   A number in scientific notation has two factors.
   The first is a number equal to or greater than 1, but less than 10.
   The second is a power of 10.

   $1{,}604{,}000 = 1.604 \times 10^6$ $0.00317 = 3.17 \times 10^{-3}$

4. Numbers in scientific notation can be multiplied and divided using the laws of exponents:

   $(3 \times 10^{-2})(6.1 \times 10^{-3}) = 18.3 \times 10^{-5} = 1.83 \times 10^{-4}$
   $(8.6 \times 10^8) \div (4.3 \times 10^4) = 2 \times 10^4$

① ZERO AS AN EXPONENT

EXAMPLE 1 **Find the value of the expression $3(7x^0)$.**

Strategy: **Use Key Concept 1.**

Step 1: Recall that an exponent refers only to the base directly to its left, in this case x.

Step 2: Evaluate the expression x^0: $x^0 = 1$.

Step 3: Simplify the expression.
$3(7 \cdot 1) = 3(7) = 21$

Solution: **The value of $3(7x^0) = 21$.**

2 NEGATIVE EXPONENTS

EXAMPLE 2

The portion of their $80,000 income that the Palacio family spends on vacations each year can be written as 4^{-2}. How much money do they spend on vacations?

Strategy: **Use Key Concept 2.**

Step 1: Write 4^{-2} as a fraction without a negative exponent.
$4^{-2} = \dfrac{1}{4^2}$

Step 2: Simplify $\dfrac{1}{4^2}$
$\dfrac{1}{4^2} = \dfrac{1}{16}$

Step 3: Find $\dfrac{1}{16}$ of $80,000.
$80,000 \div 16 = 5000

Solution: **The Palacio family spends $5000 on vacations.**

3 SCIENTIFIC NOTATION

EXAMPLE 3

The sun is approximately 93,000,000 miles from Earth. Write the distance in scientific notation.

Strategy: **Use Key Concept 3.**

Step 1: Remember that 93,000,000 **has** a decimal point. It is **after** the last 0.

Step 2: Move the decimal point in 93,000,000 so that the base number is a number at least 1 and less than 10.
Write 9.3 as the first factor.

Step 3: Count the number of places that you moved the decimal point to the **left**. You moved it 7 places.

Step 4: Write the second factor to show that the decimal point moved 7 places to the left: 10^7.

Solution: **In scientific notation, $93,000,000 = 9.3 \times 10^7$**

EXAMPLE 4

A centimeter is exactly 0.00001 of a kilometer. Express this number in scientific notation.

Strategy: Use Key Concept 3.

Step 1: Move the decimal point to the right so that the base number is at least 1 and less than 10.
Write 1 as the base.

Step 2: Count the number of places you moved the decimal point to the **right**. It moved 5 places.

Step 3: Write the second factor to show that the decimal point moved 5 places to the right: 10^{-5}

Solution: In scientific notation, $0.00001 = 1 \times 10^{-5}$.

Remember, if you move the decimal point to the left, the exponent is positive.
If you move the decimal point to to the right, the exponent is negative.

EXAMPLE 5

In a recent year, there were approximately 2.07×10^9 hundred dollar bills in circulation in the United States. The value of each bill can be thought of as 1×10^2 dollars. What was the total value of the hundred dollar bills in circulation?

Strategy: Use Key Concept 4.

Step 1: Write a multiplication sentence to describe the problem.
$(2.07 \times 10^9)(1 \times 10^2)$

Step 2: Multiply the bases, 2.07×1, and the exponents, $10^9 \times 10^2$.
$2.07 \times 1 = 2.07 \qquad 10^9 \times 10^2 = 10^{11}$

Solution: The total value of all the hundred dollar bills was
2.07×10^{11} dollars.

EXAMPLE 6

In the same year, Americans spent about 6.9×10^{11} dollars on food. If there were approximately 2.3×10^8 people in the country, about how much did the average American spend on food?

Strategy: Use Key Concept 4.

Step 1: Write a division sentence to describe the problem.
$(6.9 \times 10^{11}) \div (2.3 \times 10^8)$

Step 2: Divide the bases, $6.9 \div 2.3$, and divide the exponents, $10^{11} \div 10^8$.

$6.9 \div 2.3 = 3$ $10^{11} \div 10^8 = 10^3$

Solution: **The average American spent about 3×10^3 dollars, or about $3000.**

REGENTS MATH PRACTICE

1. How much greater is the value of $4(3x^0)$ than the value of $4(3x)^0$? Show your work.

2. Which of the following has the same value as y^0?
   a. $y \cdot y$ b. $y^5 \div y^4$
   c. $y \div y$ d. $y^0 \cdot y^1$

3. What is the value of $3 \cdot 3^{-2}$?
   f. -27   g. -9   h. $\frac{1}{9}$ j. $\frac{1}{3}$

4. What is the value of $(5 + 3y^0)$?
   a. 8   b. 5   c. 3   d. 0

5. If 0.000351 is written as 3.51×10^n, what is the value of n?
   f. 4   g. 3   h. -3   j. -4

6. In a city, there are approximately 2,750,000 telephone numbers. Which of the following names the number in scientific notation?
   a. 27.5×10^5 b. 2.75×10^6
   c. 2.75×10^5 d. 27.5×10^6

7. One estimate of the number of grains of sand on Jones Beach in Long Island is 2.23×10^{12}. Which of the following names the number in standard notation?
   f. 22,300,000,000
   g. 223,000,000,000
   h. 2,230,000,000,000
   j. 2,230,000,000

8. The weight of one of the lightest insects is a wasp with a mass of 0.000000005 kilograms. What is the mass in scientific notation?
   a. 5×10^9 b. 5×10^8
   c. 5×10^{-8} d. 5×10^{-9}

9. Express the product in scientific notation:

   $(6.2 \times 10^3) \times (3.1 \times 10^5)$

10. Express the quotient in scientific notation:

    $(9.3 \times 10^6) \div (3.1 \times 10^5)$

LESSON 9 FACTORING

KEY CONCEPTS YOU'LL NEED IN THIS LESSON

1. If terms of a polynomial have a common factor, each term can be divided by that factor. The factored form can be written using the Distributive Property.

   $$6m^3 + 2m^2n - 8m = 2m(3m^2 + mn - 4)$$

   Note that $2m$ is the greatest common factor (GCF) of the three terms in the polynomial.

2. If a **binomial** has the form $a^2 - b^2$, it is the difference of two perfect squares. It can be factored as $(a + b)(a - b)$.

   $$25r^4q^2 - 4r^2q^2 = (5r^2q + 2rq)(5r^2q - 2rq)$$

   Note that 25 and 4 are both perfect squares, and that each variable has an even exponent.

3. A **trinomial** in the form $ax^2 + bx + c$ can be factored into two binomials.

   $$x^2 - 5x - 24 = (x - 8)(x + 3)$$

   Note the following:
   - x^2 has been factored in to $x \cdot x$: $(x \quad)(x \quad)$
   - -24 has been factored into -8 and +3: $(x - 8)(x + 3)$

   There are other factor pairs of -24: +8 and -3, +6 and -4, +4 and -6, +12 and -2, and so on. But only -8 and +3 have a sum of -5, which is needed for the middle term.

4. Some polynomials can be factored using a combination of Key Concepts 1 and 2 or 1 and 3.

   $$3m^2 - 48 \quad \rightarrow \quad 3(m^2 - 16) \quad \rightarrow \quad 3(m + 4)(m - 4)$$
   Key Concept 1   Key Concept 2

   $$6n^2 + 12n + 6 \quad \rightarrow \quad 6(n^2 + 2n + 1) \quad \rightarrow \quad 6(n + 1)(n + 1)$$
   Key Concept 1   Key Concept 2

---

1   FINDING A COMMON FACTOR

EXAMPLE 1

Factor the polynomial.

$$4x^2y^3 - 2y^2 + 6xy$$

Strategy: **Use Key Concept 1.**

Step 1: Find the GCF of the terms in the polynomial.
First find the GCF of the numerical coefficients 4, 2, and 6.
The GCF of 4, 2, and 6 is 2.

Then find the GCF of the variable parts: x^2y^3, y^2, and xy.
The GCF of x^2y^3, y^2, and xy is y.
So, the GCF of the three terms is $2y$.

Step 2: Divide each term of the polynomial by the GCF.
$$\frac{4x^2y^3 - 2y^2 + 6xy}{2y} = 2x^2y^2 - y + 3x$$

Step 3: Use the Distributive Property to write the polynomial in factored form.
$2y(2x^2y^2 - y + 3x)$

Solution: $4x^2y^3 - 2y^2 + 6xy = 2y(2x^2y^2 - y + 3x)$

---

2 FACTORING THE DIFFERENCE OF TWO PERFECT SQUARES

EXAMPLE 2   **Factor the binomial $100 - 25x^2$.**

Strategy: **Use Key Concept 2.**

Step 1: Since the binomial is in the form $a^2 - b^2$, factor it to $(a + b)(a - b)$:
$100 - 25x^2 = (10 + 5x)(10 - 5x)$

Solution: **$100 - 25x^2 = (10 + 5x)(10 - 5x)$**

Ask yourself the following when you need to factor a binomial:

- *Is each term a perfect square?*
- *Is the binomial the difference of two perfect squares?*

---

3 FACTORING A TRINOMIAL

EXAMPLE 3   **Factor the trinomial $x^2 - 13x + 36$.**

Strategy: **Use Key Concept 3.**

Step 1: Factor x^2: $(x \quad)(x \quad)$

Step 2: Look for factor pairs of 36. Since 36 is positive, the factors will have the same signs, either both positive or both negative.

The possible pairs are:
36 and 1, 18 and 2, 12 and 3, 9 and 4, 6 and 6,
as well as
-36 and -1, -18 and -2, -12 and -3, -9 and -4, and -6 and -6.

Step 3: Choose the only factor pair that has a sum of -13 which is needed for the middle term.
Only -9 and -4 add to -13.

Step 4: Write the factored form: $(x - 9)(x - 4)$

Solution: $x^2 - 13x + 36 = (x - 9)(x - 4)$

EXAMPLE 4

Factor the trinomial $2x^2 + x - 3$.

Strategy: **Use Key Concept 3.**

Step 1: As in Example 3, factor $2x^2$: $(2x\quad)(x\quad)$

Step 2: Again, consider the final term, -3. Since the sign is negative, one factor will be positive and the other will be negative. Because 3 is a prime, the only possible factor pairs are:
-3 and +1,   +3 and -1,   +1 and -3,   and   -1 and +3.
The order is important here, because the first terms of each factor are different: $2x$ and x.

Step 3: Test each possible factor pair to find the one in which the sum will be +1, the coefficient of the term x:

$$\underbrace{(2x \overbrace{- 3)(x + 1}^{-3x})}_{+2x} \quad \mathbf{\underbrace{(2x \overbrace{+ 3)(x - 1}^{+3x})}_{-2x}} \quad \underbrace{(2x \overbrace{+ 1)(x - 3}^{+1x})}_{-6x} \quad \underbrace{(2x \overbrace{- 1)(x + 3}^{-1x})}_{+6x}$$

$-3x + (+2x) = -1x$ **$3x + (-2x) = +1x$** $+1x + (-6x) = -5x$ $-1x + (+6x) = +5x$

Since only the second set of factors (+3 and -1) multiply to -3 and add to +1, use them.

Step 4: Write the factored form of the polynomial: $(2x + 3)(x - 1)$

Solution: $2x^2 + x - 3 = (2x + 3)(x - 1)$

EXAMPLE 5

Factor $3x^2 - 6x - 45$.

Strategy: **Use Key Concepts 4, 1, and 2.**

Step 1: Look for a factor that is common to all three terms. Each term can be divided by 3.

Step 2: Divide each term by the common factor, 3.
$3x^2 - 6x - 45 = 3(x^2 - 2x - 15)$

Step 3: Factor the trinomial.
$x^2 - 2x - 15 = (x - 5)(x + 3)$

Solution: $3x^2 - 6x - 45 = 3(x - 5)(x + 3)$

EXAMPLE 6

Factor $36m^2 - 100n^2$.

Strategy: **Use Key Concepts 4, 1, and 3.**

Step 1: Look for a common factor
Each term can be divided by 4.

Step 2: Divide each term by the common factor, 4.
$36m^2 - 100n^2 = 4(9m^2 - 25n^2)$

Step 3: Factor the binomial.
$9m^2 - 25n^2 = (3m + 5n)(3m - 5n)$

Solution: $36m^2 - 100n^2 = 4(3m + 5n)(3m - 5n)$

Remember, when factoring any polynomial:
- *First factor out any term that is common to all terms,* ***then***
- *Try to factor a trinomial into* —OR— • *If a binomial is not the difference*
  two binomials. *of two perfect squares, it cannot be*
  factored further.

REGENTS MATH PRACTICE

Factor completely.

1. $m^2 - n^2$

2. $2x^2 - 2x - 60$

3. $x^2 - 6x + 9$

4. $2n^2 - 50$

5. $3m^3 - 6m^2 + 9m$

6. $4a^2b - 5a^2c^2 + 6ad^2$

7. $5x^2y^2 - 15xy + 20xyz$

8. $12m^2n^3 - 18m^2n^2 - 24m^4n^4$

9. $169c^6 - 121d^2$

10. $81 - 9y^4$

11. $a^4 - a^2$

12. $y^2 - 8y + 16$

13. $3x^2 - x - 2$

14. $5a^2 - 9a - 2$

15. $4x^2 - 8x + 3$

16. $6n^2 + n - 12$

17. $3x^2 - 12x - 36$

18. $x^2 - 14x + 33$

19. $4r^8 - 9x^4$

20. $m^3 - m$

LESSON 10
FRACTION OPERATIONS

KEY CONCEPTS YOU'LL NEED IN THIS LESSON

1. A fraction is said to be **undefined** when its denominator is 0. This is because division by 0 is undefined—that is, it has no consistent meaning within the system of mathematics. (If division by 0 were permitted, you could "prove" nonsense propositions like "1 = 2".) The fraction $\frac{x-2}{x+2}$ is undefined when $x = -2$ because if $x = -2$, then the denominator $x + 2 = 0$.

2. To **simplify a fraction to lowest terms**, factor the numerator and denominator. Then cancel all **factors** that are common to both the numerator and denominator.

$$\frac{9x^2 + 6x + 1}{9x^2 - 1} \rightarrow \frac{\overset{1}{\cancel{(3x+1)}}(3x+1)}{\underset{1}{\cancel{(3x+1)}}(3x-1)} \rightarrow \frac{3x+1}{3x-1}$$

3. a To **add or subtract fractions with like denominators**, combine the numerators. Keep the same denominator. Finally, simplify the fraction to lowest terms, if possible.

   b To **add or subtract fractions with different denominators**, use the least common denominator (LCD) to write the fractions with like denominators. Then proceed as above.

$$\frac{3}{2x} + \frac{4}{5x} = \frac{5}{5} \cdot \frac{3}{2x} + \frac{4}{5x} \cdot \frac{2}{2} = \frac{15+8}{10x} = \frac{23}{10x}$$

Since the LCD of $2x$ and $5x$ is $10x$, multiply each fraction by what is needed to make each denominator $10x$.

4. To **multiply algebraic fractions**, follow the same steps used to multiply numerical fractions: factor each numerator and denominator if possible, cancel common factors, then multiply numerators and denominators.

$$\frac{a^2 - 81}{a^2 - 64} \cdot \frac{a^2 - 8a}{a - 9} \rightarrow \frac{(a+9)\overset{1}{\cancel{(a-9)}}}{(a+8)\underset{1}{\cancel{(a-8)}}} \cdot \frac{a\overset{1}{\cancel{(a-8)}}}{\underset{1}{\cancel{a-9}}} \rightarrow \frac{a(a+9)}{a+8}$$

5. To **divide algebraic fractions**, follow the same steps used to divide numerical fractions: invert the divisor and proceed as though you were multiplying.

$$\frac{x-y}{x^3 + xy^2} \div \frac{x^2 - y^2}{x^2y + y^3} \rightarrow \frac{x-y}{x^3 + xy^2} \cdot \frac{x^2y + y^3}{x^2 - y^2} \rightarrow \frac{x-y}{x(x^2 + y^2)} \cdot \frac{y(x^2 + y^2)}{(x+y)(x-y)} \rightarrow \frac{y}{x(x+y)}$$

1   SIMPLIFYING FRACTIONS

EXAMPLE 1

Simplify to lowest terms:

$$\frac{4x + 12}{x^2 + 7x + 12}$$

Strategy: **Use Key Concept 2.**

Step 1: Factor both the numerator and denominator.

$$\frac{4x + 12}{x^2 + 7x + 12} = \frac{4(x + 3)}{(x + 4)(x + 3)}$$

Step 2: Cancel common factors.

$$\frac{4x + 12}{x^2 + 7x + 12} = \frac{4\overset{1}{\cancel{(x + 3)}}}{(x + 4)\underset{1}{\cancel{(x + 3)}}} = \frac{4}{(x + 4)}$$

Solution: $\dfrac{4x + 12}{x^2 + 7x + 12} = \dfrac{4}{(x + 4)}$ **if** $x \neq$ **-4**

(If x were to equal -4, the denominator would then be 0.)

2   ADDING AND SUBTRACTING FRACTIONS

EXAMPLE 2

Find the sum.

$$\frac{5m}{4x} + \frac{3m}{4x} + \frac{7}{4x}$$

Strategy: **Use Key Concept 3a.**

Step 1: Write the numerators over the denominator. Then add the numerators.

$$\frac{5m}{4x} + \frac{3m}{4x} + \frac{7}{4x} = \frac{5m + 3m + 7}{4x} = \frac{8m + 7}{4x}$$

Solution: $\dfrac{5m}{4x} + \dfrac{3m}{4x} + \dfrac{7}{4x} = \dfrac{8m + 7}{4x}$ **if** $x \neq 0$

EXAMPLE 3

Find the difference.

$$\frac{6}{3x} - \frac{7y}{5x}$$

Strategy: **Use Key Concept 3b.**

Step 1: Find the LCD of $3x$ and $5x$. The LCD is $15x$.

Step 2: Multiply each fraction by what is needed to make each denominator $15x$.

$$\frac{6}{3x} - \frac{7y}{5x} = \frac{5}{5} \cdot \frac{6}{3x} - \frac{7y}{5x} \cdot \frac{3}{3} = \frac{30}{15x} - \frac{21y}{15x}$$

Step 3: Combine the numerators over the denominator, $15x$.

$$\frac{30 - 21y}{15x}$$

Solution: $\dfrac{6}{3x} - \dfrac{7y}{5x} = \dfrac{30 - 21y}{15x}$ if $x \neq 0$

EXAMPLE 4 Add $\dfrac{1}{x+3} + \dfrac{1}{x+4}$

Strategy: **Use Key Concept 3b.**

Step 1: Find the LCD of $x + 3$ and $x + 4$.
The LCD is $(x + 3)(x + 4)$.

Step 2: Multiply each fraction as needed to form fractions that both have the LCD as their denominator.

$$\frac{(x+4)}{(x+4)} \cdot \frac{1}{(x+3)} + \frac{1}{(x+4)} \cdot \frac{(x+3)}{(x+3)} = \frac{(x+4)+(x+3)}{(x+4)(x+3)} = \frac{2x+7}{(x+4)(x+3)}$$

Solution: $\dfrac{1}{x+3} + \dfrac{1}{x+4} = \dfrac{2x+7}{(x+4)(x+3)}$ if $x \neq -4$ and $x \neq -3$

---

3 MULTIPLYING AND DIVIDING FRACTIONS

EXAMPLE 5 **Find the quotient.**

$$\frac{10x - 70}{3a - 9} \div \frac{5x - 35}{6a - 18}$$

Strategy: **Use Key Concepts 4 and 5.**

Step 1: Invert the divisor.

$$\frac{10x - 70}{3a - 9} \div \frac{5x - 35}{6a - 18} = \frac{10x - 70}{3a - 9} \cdot \frac{6a - 18}{5x - 35}$$

Step 2: Factor each numerator and denominator.

$$\frac{10(x - 7)}{3(a - 3)} \cdot \frac{6(a - 3)}{5(x - 7)}$$

Step 3:   Cancel and multiply.

$$\frac{\overset{2}{\cancel{10}}\overset{1}{\cancel{(x-7)}}}{\underset{1}{\cancel{3}}\underset{1}{\cancel{(a-3)}}} \cdot \frac{\overset{2}{\cancel{6}}\overset{1}{\cancel{(a-3)}}}{\underset{1}{\cancel{5}}\underset{1}{\cancel{(x-7)}}} = \frac{2 \times 2}{1 \times 1} = \frac{4}{1} = 4$$

Solution: $\dfrac{10x - 70}{3a - 9} \cdot \dfrac{6a - 18}{5x - 35} = 4$

REGENTS MATH PRACTICE

In questions 1–3, simplify the fraction.

1. $\dfrac{25x^5}{125x^7y}$

2. $\dfrac{m^2n - mn^2}{9m - 9n}$

3. $\dfrac{9r^2 + 6r + 1}{9r^2 + 1}$

In questions 4–6, combine the fractions.

4. $\dfrac{5}{3x} - \dfrac{4}{4x}$

5. $\dfrac{7a}{3b} - \dfrac{5a}{7b}$

6. $\dfrac{5}{x + y} + \dfrac{6}{x - y}$

In questions 7–10, find the product or quotient. Write the answer in simplest from.

7. $\dfrac{a^3b^4}{36} \cdot \dfrac{24}{a^4b^3}$

8. $\dfrac{2m + 10}{6n - 24} \cdot \dfrac{7n - 28}{4m + 20}$

9. $\dfrac{a^2 - 25}{2b + 4} \div \dfrac{a^2 - 25}{b^2 + 4}$

10. $\dfrac{7r + 14r}{5s^2} \div \dfrac{28r}{15s^3}$

LESSON 11
OPERATIONS WITH RADICALS

KEY CONCEPTS YOU'LL NEED IN THIS LESSON

1. Finding a **square root** of a number is the opposite of raising the number to a power.

   The inverse of $4^2 = 16$ is $\sqrt{16} = 4$ (read "the square root of 16 equals 4").

   In general, the **principal square root** of a number is positive. However, the square root of a number can be negative.
   $$\sqrt{25} = +5 \text{ since } (+5)(+5) = 25 \qquad \text{or}$$
   $$\sqrt{25} = -5 \text{ since } (-5)(-5) = 25$$

2. **Radicals** can be simplified. Look for the greatest factor of the **radicand** (the number under the radical sign) that is a perfect square. Factor the radicand and use the square root of the perfect square.

   In $\sqrt{72}$, 72 is the radicand.
   $$\sqrt{72} = \sqrt{36 \cdot 2} = \sqrt{36} \cdot \sqrt{2} = 6\sqrt{2} \text{ (read "6 times the square root of 2")}$$

   A radical is in simplest form when the greatest perfect square factor of the radicand is 1.

   $\sqrt{15}$ is in simplest form since the only factor of 15 that is a perfect square is 1.

3. **Like radicals** can be combined by addition or subtraction.

   $\sqrt{7} + 5\sqrt{7}$ are like radicals since the radicands are the same.

   $\sqrt{7} + 5\sqrt{7} = 6\sqrt{7}$

   $9\sqrt{2} - \sqrt{50}$ can be simplified to become like radicals.

   $9\sqrt{2} - \sqrt{25 \cdot 2} = 9\sqrt{2} - 5\sqrt{2} = (9 - 5)\sqrt{2} = 4\sqrt{2}$

4. Any two radicals can be combined by multiplication or division.

   a. $2\sqrt{8} \cdot 3\sqrt{10} = 2 \cdot 3\sqrt{8}\sqrt{10}$ Rearrange the terms using the commutative property.

   $\qquad\qquad\qquad = 6\sqrt{80}$ Multiply coefficients and radicands.

   $6\sqrt{16 \cdot 5} = 6 \cdot 4\sqrt{5} = 24\sqrt{5}$ Simplify.

   b. $\dfrac{6\sqrt{75}}{2\sqrt{3}} = \dfrac{6}{2}\sqrt{\dfrac{75}{3}} = 3\sqrt{25} = 3 \cdot 5 = 15$

1 SIMPLIFYING RADICALS

EXAMPLE 1

Simplify the expression: $7\sqrt{20}$

Strategy: **Use Key Concepts 1 and 2.**

Step 1: Write the radicand 20 as the product of two factors. One of the factors should be the greatest possible perfect square.

$7\sqrt{20} = 7\sqrt{4 \cdot 5}$

Step 2: Find the square root of 4, the greatest factor of 20 that is a perfect square.

$7\sqrt{20} = 7 \cdot \sqrt{4} \cdot \sqrt{5} = 7 \cdot 2\sqrt{5}$

Step 3: Multiply the coefficients 7 and 2.
$7 \cdot 2\sqrt{5} = 14\sqrt{5}$

Solution: **In simplest form, $7\sqrt{20} = 14\sqrt{5}$.**

EXAMPLE 2

Simplify $\sqrt{9x^3}$.

Strategy: **Use Key Concepts 1 and 2.**

Step 1: Factor the radicand so that one of the factors is the greatest possible perfect square.

$$\sqrt{9x^3} = \sqrt{9x^2 \cdot x} = \sqrt{9x^2} \cdot \sqrt{x}$$

Step 2: Find the square root of $\sqrt{9x^2}$ and use it as the coefficient.

$$\sqrt{9x^2} = 3x$$

Solution: **In simplest form, $\sqrt{9x^2} = 3x\sqrt{x}$.**

2 ADDITION AND SUBTRACTION

EXAMPLE 3

Find the sum: $9\sqrt{8} + 3\sqrt{18}$

Strategy: **Use Key Concepts 2 and 3.**

| **Step 1:** | If possible, simplify the radicals to make them like radicals. |

$$9\sqrt{8} \;=\; 9\sqrt{4 \cdot 2} \;=\; 9 \cdot 2\sqrt{2} \;=\; 18\sqrt{2}$$
$$3\sqrt{18} \;=\; 3\sqrt{9 \cdot 2} \;=\; 3 \cdot 3\sqrt{2} \;=\; 9\sqrt{2}$$

| **Step 2:** | Since the two terms have like radicals, they can be combined by using the Distributive Property. |

$$18\sqrt{2} + 9\sqrt{2} = (18 + 9)\sqrt{2} = 27\sqrt{2}$$

| **Solution:** | $9\sqrt{8} + 3\sqrt{18} = 27\sqrt{2}$ |

EXAMPLE 4

Find the difference: $\sqrt{36a} - \sqrt{16a}$

| **Strategy:** | **Use Key Concepts 2 and 3.** |

| **Step 1:** | As above, simplify each radical if possible. |

$$\sqrt{36a} = \sqrt{36 \cdot a} = \sqrt{36} \cdot \sqrt{a} = 6\sqrt{a}$$
$$\sqrt{16a} = \sqrt{16 \cdot a} = r(16) \cdot \sqrt{a} = 4\sqrt{a}$$

| **Step 2:** | Combine the like radicals using the Distributive Property. |

$$6\sqrt{a} - 4\sqrt{a} = (6 - 4)\sqrt{a} = 2\sqrt{a}$$

| **Solution:** | $\sqrt{36a} - \sqrt{16a} = 2\sqrt{a}$ |

3 · MULTIPLICATION AND DIVISION

EXAMPLE 5

Multiply: $\sqrt{16x^2} \cdot \sqrt{4x}$

| **Strategy:** | **Use Key Concepts 2 and 4.** |

| **Step 1:** | Multiply the radicands. |

$$\sqrt{16x^2} \cdot \sqrt{4x} = \sqrt{16 \cdot 4 \cdot x^2 \cdot x} = \sqrt{64x^3}$$

| **Step 2:** | Simplify. |

$$\sqrt{64x^3} = \sqrt{64x^2 \cdot x} = \sqrt{64x^2} \cdot \sqrt{x} = 8x\sqrt{x}$$

| **Solution:** | $\sqrt{16x^2} \cdot \sqrt{4x} = 8x\sqrt{x}$ |

EXAMPLE 6

Divide: $8\sqrt{48} \div 2\sqrt{3}$

Strategy: Use Key Concepts 2 and 4.

Step 1: Write the division problem as a fraction.

$$\frac{8\sqrt{48}}{2\sqrt{3}}$$

Step 2: Write the radical as a fraction.

$$\frac{8}{2}\sqrt{\frac{48}{3}}$$

Step 3: Simplify the radical.

$$\frac{8}{2}\sqrt{\frac{48}{3}} = 4\sqrt{16} = 4 \cdot 4 = 16$$

Solution: $8\sqrt{48} \div 2\sqrt{3} = 16$

REGENTS MATH PRACTICE

In questions 1–4, simplify the expression.

1. $2\sqrt{80}$

2. $14\sqrt{128}$

3. $3\sqrt{200}$

4. $7\sqrt{32}$

In questions 5–7, combine the expressions.

5. $\sqrt{98} + 2\sqrt{8}$

6. $\sqrt{12x^2} + 3\sqrt{27x^2}$

7. $\sqrt{64}\,m + \sqrt{100}\,m - \sqrt{16}\,m$

In questions 8–10, multiply or divide. Write the product or quotient in simplest form.

8. $(4\sqrt{6})(9\sqrt{3})$

9. $(\sqrt{16x^3})^2$

10. $\dfrac{15\sqrt{50}}{3\sqrt{2}}$

LESSON 12
THE PYTHAGOREAN THEOREM

KEY CONCEPTS YOU'LL NEED IN THIS LESSON

1. In a right triangle, the square of the hypotenuse (the longest side) is equal to the sum of the squares of the two legs (the two shorter sides).

In right triangle ABC, $c^2 = a^2 + b^2$

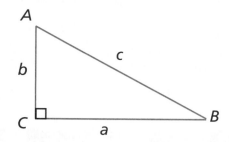

2. A triangle can be shown to be a right triangle by using the converse of the above statement.

   If $c^2 = a^2 + b^2$ in a triangle, then the triangle is a right triangle.

---

1 FINDING MISSING LENGTHS

EXAMPLE 1

In a right triangle, the length of the hypotenuse is 51 in. and one leg is 24 in. Find the length of the other leg.

Strategy: Use Key Concept 1.

Step 1: Apply the Pythagorean Theorem to the given side lengths.

$$c^2 = a^2 + b^2$$

$$51^2 = 24^2 + b^2$$

$$2{,}601 = 576 + b^2$$

$$2{,}025 = b^2$$

$$\sqrt{2{,}025} = b$$

$$45 = b$$

Solution: The length of the other leg of the triangle is 45 in.

EXAMPLE 2

The two shorter sides of a right triangle are 4 and $3\sqrt{2}$. Find the length of the hypotenuse.

Strategy: Use Key Concept 1.

Step 1: Substitute the given values into the Pythagorean formula.

$c^2 = a^2 + b^2$

$c^2 = 4^2 + (3\sqrt{2})^2$

$c^2 = 16 + (3\sqrt{2})(3\sqrt{2})$

$c^2 = 16 + 3(3)(\sqrt{2})(\sqrt{2})$

$c^2 = 16 + 9(2) \quad = \quad 16 + 18 \quad = \quad 34$

$c = \sqrt{34}$

Solution: The length of the hypotenuse is $\sqrt{34}$ or 5.8 rounded to the nearest tenth.

EXAMPLE 3

A triangle has the following side lengths: 7, 17, and 22. Is the triangle a right triangle?

Strategy: Use Key Concept 2.

Step 1: Test the side lengths to see whether the Pythagorean Theorem applies.

$c^2 = a^2 + b^2$

$\quad\quad ?$

$22^2 = 17^2 + 7^2$

$484 = 289 + 49$

$484 \neq 338$

Solution: The triangle is not a right triangle.

EXAMPLE 4

A 26-ft-long ramp is used to reach 10 ft up a wall. The ramp covers a horizontal distance of 24 ft. To make the ramp less steep, the horizontal distance is doubled. To reach the same 10 ft height, how long will the ramp need to be? Show the answer in radical form and rounded to the nearest hundredth foot.

Strategy: Use Key Concept 1.

Step 1: Apply the Pythagorean Theorem.
The new horizontal distance will be 48 ft. The height (10 ft) remains the same.

$c^2 = a^2 + b^2$

$c^2 = 48^2 + 10^2$

$c^2 = 2{,}304 + 100 = 2404$

$c = \sqrt{2{,}404}$

Solution: **The length of the ramp must be $\sqrt{2{,}404}$ or about 49.03 ft.**

REGENTS MATH PRACTICE

1. Find the length of the diagonal of a square whose side measures 10 cm. Write the answer in simplest radical form.

2. Find the length of the diagonal of a rectangle whose sides measure 20 ft and 48 ft.

3. Two sides of a right triangle measure 14 in. and 50 in. If all sides are whole number lengths, find the length of the third side.

4. The length of a diagonal of a rectangle is 16. One side of the rectangle is 8. Find the length of the other side.

5. The perimeter of a square is 48 cm. Find the length of the diagonal of the square. Round the answer to the nearest hundredth cm.

6. The diagonal of a square is $15\sqrt{2}$ Find the length of a side of the square. Explain how you solved the problem.

In problems 7–10, the side lengths of a triangle are given. Determine whether or not each triangle is a right triangle.

7. 36, 60, 48

8. 6, 3, $3\sqrt{2}$

9. 6, 7, 11

10. 12, 8, $2\sqrt{20}$

UNIT ② REVIEW

1. Which of the following operations gives the greatest result?
   a. -8×-2 b. $-8 + -2$
   c. $-8 - 2$ d. $-8 \div -2$

2. In simplifying the following expression, which operation would you perform last?
   $18 - 6 \div (2 + 1) \times 2$
   f. addition   g. multiplication
   h. subtraction   j. division

3. If the weight of a cat is $(2x^2 - 4)$ pounds and the weight of a dog is $(5x^2 + 7)$ pounds, which expression names the difference in their weights in pounds?
   a. $7x + 3$ b. $7x^2 + 3$
   c. $3x^2 + 3$ d. $3x^2 + 11$

4. In Question 3 above, explain how you could check your answer by substituting a value for x in the weights of the dog and cat.

5. A milk storage tank holds $8m^3 - 16m^2 + 4$ gallons. When it is half full, what is an expression for the number of quarts of milk in the tank?
   a. $m^3 - 4m^2 + 1$
   b. $4m^3 - 8m^2 + 2$
   c. $16m^3 - 32m^2 + 8$
   d. $32m^3 - 64m^2 + 16$

6. What is the value of $a^2 + b(a^2 - b)$ when $a = 2$ and $b = -3$?
   f. 49   g. 7   h. -17   j. -21

7. Which expressions have the same value as $5x^0$?
   1) $(5x)^0$ 2) $(4x + 1)^0$
   3) $5(x)^0$ 4) $5(3x)^0$
   a. 1 and 4 only
   b. 1 and 3 only
   c. 2 and 4 only
   d. 3 and 4 only

8. Which expression is factored completely?
   f. $8x^2 - 18y^4 = 2(2x + 3y^2)(2x - 3y^2)$
   g. $100 - 25y^6 = (10 + 5y^3)(10 - 5y^3)$
   h. $8e^2 + 4e - 12 = 2(4e^2 + 2e - 6)$
   j. $45n^2 - 125 = 5(9n^2 - 25)$

9. Which is the least common denominator for the following fractions?
   $$\frac{4}{3x} + \frac{7}{4x} + \frac{2a}{5x^2}$$
   a. $10x^2$ b. $45x$ c. $45x^2$ d. $60x^2$

10. Which expression is equivalent to $\sqrt{25m} - \sqrt{16m}$?
    f. $3m$ g. $\sqrt{m}$ h. $9\sqrt{m}$ j. $\sqrt{9m}$

11. The diagonal of a square measures $\sqrt{128}$. What is the length of a side of the square?
    a. $\sqrt{8}$ b. 8   c. $\sqrt{16}$ d. 16

LESSON ⑬ EQUATIONS

KEY CONCEPTS YOU'LL NEED IN THIS LESSON

1. To **solve an equation** means to get the variable alone on one side of the equals sign. When you do that, whatever is on the other side is the solution.

2. Use **inverse operations** to "take an equation apart."
   Addition and subtraction are inverse operations; each undoes the other.
   Multiplication and division are inverse operations; each undoes the other.

3. When an equation requires **more than one operation**, first undo addition or subtraction, then multiplication or division.

$$7m + 4 = 46$$
$$\underline{ - 4 \quad - 4} \quad \text{Undo addition of 4.}$$
$$\frac{7m}{7} \quad = \quad \frac{42}{7} \quad \text{Undo multiplication by 7.}$$
$$m \quad = \quad 6$$

4. **Parentheses in an equation** can be removed by using the Distributive Property.

$$2(x - 3) + 5 = 15$$

$2x - 6 + 5 = 15$	Use the distributive property.
$2x - 1 = 15$	Combine like terms (-6 and +5).
$2x = 16$	Undo subtracting 1.
$x = 8$	Undo multiplying by 2.

5. When an equation has the **variable on both sides of the equals sign**, get the variable terms on one side and the numerical terms on the other. Remember, variable terms can be treated like numbers, which is what they represent.

$$2x - 7 = 5x - 19$$

$\underline{ + 7 \qquad + 7}$		Undo subtracting 7.
$2x = 5x - 12$		
$\underline{- 2x = -2x }$		Remove the variable from one side.
$0 = 3x - 12$		
$\underline{+ 12 \qquad + 12}$		Undo subtracting 12.
$12 = 3x$		
$\dfrac{12}{3} = \dfrac{3x}{3}$		Undo multiplying by 3.
$4 = x$		

6. You can graph the solution set of an equation on a **number line**. In the equation in Key Concept 5, where the solution is $x = 4$, the graph of the solution is

The solid dot at 4 in the graph shows that the solution set consists of only the number 4.

> *Remember, to keep an equality, whatever you do to one side of an equation, do the same to the other side.*

1 USING INVERSE OPERATIONS

EXAMPLE 1

Solve and check:
$5x - 9 = 26$

Strategy: Use Key Concepts 1, 2, and 3.

Step 1: Undo subtracting 9. Use addition.
$$5x - 9 = 26$$
$$\underline{+9 \qquad +9}$$
$$5x \quad = 35$$

Step 2: Undo multiplying by 5. Use division.
$$\frac{5x}{5} = \frac{35}{5}$$
$$x = 7$$

Step 3: Check the solution. Substitute the value 7 for x in the original equation.
$$5x - 9 = 26$$
$$5(7) - 9 = 26$$
$$35 - 9 = 26$$
$$26 = 26 \checkmark \qquad \text{The value } x = 7 \text{ makes the equation true.}$$

Solution: If $5x - 9 = 26$, then $x = 7$.

2 EQUATIONS WITH PARENTHESES

EXAMPLE 2

Solve and check. Graph the solution.
$8x - (5x - 2) = 14$

Strategy: Use Key Concepts 2, 3, 4, and 6.

Step 1:   Use the Distributive Property to eliminate the parentheses. Since there is no number directly in front of the parentheses, assume there is a 1.

$8x - 1(5x - 2) = 14$

$8x - 5x + 2 = 14$ Use the Distributive Property. Pay careful attention to signs.

Step 2:   Combine like terms.

$8x - 5x + 2 = 14$

$3x + 2 = 14$ Subtract $8x - 5x$. Use the Distributive Property. $8x - 5x = (8 - 5)x = 3x$

Step 3:   Undo the addition.

$3x + 2 - 2 = 14 - 2$

$3x = 12$

Step 4:   Undo the multiplication.

$\dfrac{3x}{3} = \dfrac{12}{3}$

$x = 4$

Step 5:   Check the solution, $x = 4$.

$8x - (5x - 2) = 14$

$8(4) - (5(4) - 2) = 14$

$32 - (20 - 2) = 14$

$32 - 18 = 14$

$14 = 14$ ✔

Step 6:   Graph the solution.

Solution: **If $8x - (5x - 2) = 14$, then $x = 4$.**

(**EXAMPLE 2**)

Solve and check. Graph the solution.

$\dfrac{3}{4}(8x - 12) = 7x - 11$

Strategy: **Use Key Concepts 3, 4, and 5.**

Step 1:   Remove the parentheses. Use the Distributive Property.

$\dfrac{3}{4}(8x - 12) = 7x - 11$

$6x - 9 = 7x - 11$

Step 2: Remove the variable term from one side.

$$6x - 9 = 7x - 11$$
$$\underline{-6x \qquad -6x} \qquad \text{Subtract } 6x \text{ from each side.}$$
$$-9 = x - 11$$

Step 3: Get the variable by itself.

$$-9 = x - 11$$
$$\underline{+11 \qquad +11} \qquad \text{Undo subtracting 11 by adding 11.}$$
$$2 = x$$

Step 4: Check the solution.

$$\frac{3}{4}(8x - 12) = 7x - 11$$

$$\frac{3}{4}(8(2) - 12) = 7(2) - 11$$

$$\frac{3}{4}(16 - 12) = 14 - 11$$

$$\frac{3}{4}(4) = 3$$

$$3 = 3 ✔$$

Step 5: Graph the solution.

Solution: If $\frac{3}{4}(8x - 12) = 7x - 11$, then $x = 2$.

REGENTS MATH PRACTICE

Solve, check, and graph the solution to each equation.

1. $\frac{x}{3} = 8$

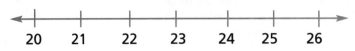

2. $5y = -20$

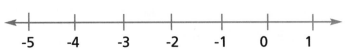

3. $6m + 4 = -8$

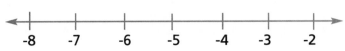

4. $\frac{1}{5}w - 3 = 7$

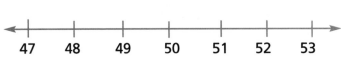

5. $t - 23 = -31$

Solve and check the solution to each equation.

6. $r + \frac{1}{3} = 2\frac{2}{3}$

7. $\frac{n}{7} + 6 = 13$

8. $2x - 3 = -39$

9. $5(z - 9) = 25$

10. $5m + 8(2m - 9) = 54$

11. $3(w - 5) - 12 = 9$

12. $9e - 2(4e + 1) = 4$

13. $7h - (h - 4) = 34$

14. $17 - 3(x - 2) = -7$

15. $6x - 3 = 3x + 9$

16. $5w + 3 = 12 + 2w$

17. $4n - 15 = 11n - 1$

18. $6(r - 9) = 4(2r - 15)$

19. $12 - (x + 2) = x + 14$

20. $7 - 2y = y - 11$

LESSON 14
SOLVING PROBLEMS WITH ONE EQUATION

KEY CONCEPTS YOU'LL NEED IN THIS LESSON

1. You can **represent the missing value or values** in a problem (**the unknown or unknowns**) by any variable you choose. Once you identify one unknown by a variable, the other unknown must relate to the first.

   Consider the following problem:

   The larger of two numbers is 20 more than 3 times the smaller. If the larger number is increased by the smaller, the result is 84. Find the numbers.

   Let the smaller number = x.
   Then, the larger number = $3x + 20$ (or 20 more than 3 times x).

2. You can **write a word equation** to represent the relationships described in the problem. You can then use the word equation to write an **algebraic equation**.

If the larger number	is increased by	the smaller,	the result is	84.
$3x + 20$	**+**	**x**	**=**	**84**

3. To **solve a problem**, solve the algebraic equation for the variable. Then use that value to find the other value(s).

   $$3x + 20 + x = 84$$
   $$4x + 20 = 84 \qquad \text{Combine like terms.}$$
   $$4x = 64 \qquad \text{Subtract 20.}$$
   $$x = 16 \qquad \text{Divide by 4.}$$

   Since $x = 16$, $3x + 20 = 3(16) + 20 = 68$.

4. You can **check a solution** by comparing your answers to the problem conditions.

   The larger of two numbers is 20 more than 3 times the smaller.
   $68 = 3(16) + 20 \qquad 68 = 68$ ✔

   The sum of the two numbers is 84.
   $16 + 68 = 84 \qquad 84 = 84$ ✔

1 NUMBER PROBLEMS

EXAMPLE 1

If a number is decreased by 9 and the difference is multiplied by 3, the result is the same as twice the number decreased by 10. Find the number.

Strategy: **Use Key Concepts 1 – 4.**

Step 1: Represent the missing number using a variable.
Let x = the missing number. Then,
$x - 9$ = the number decreased by 9, and
$3(x - 9)$ = the difference of x and 9 multiplied by 3, and
$2x - 10$ = twice the number decreased by 10.

Step 2: Write a word equation to represent the information in the problem. Write an algebraic equation from the word equation.

If a number is decreased by 9 and the difference is multiplied by 3,	the result is the same as	twice the number decreased by 10.
$3(x - 9)$	=	$2x - 10$

Step 3: Solve the algebraic equation.
$3(x - 9) = 2x - 10$
$3x - 27 = 2x - 10$ Use the distributive property.
$x - 27 = -10$ Subtract $2x$ from each side.
$x = 17$ Add 27 to each side.

Step 4: Since there is no other value to find, check the solution.
$3(x - 9) = 2x - 10$
$3(17 - 9) = 2(17) - 10$ Substitute the value 17 for x.
$3(8) = 34 - 10$ Simplify each side.
$24 = 24$ ✔

Solution: **The number that meets the conditions in the problem is 17.**

2 CONSECUTIVE INTEGER PROBLEMS

Remember, consecutive integers follow one another in order.
Examples are -9, -8, -7 or 0, 1, 2 or, using a variable, x, x + 1, and x + 2.
Examples of consecutive even integers are 2, 4, 6 or -6, -4, -2, or x, x + 2, x + 4.
Examples of consecutive odd integers are -7, -5, -3, or 9, 11, 13, or x, x + 2, x + 4.
Note that both consecutive odd integers and consecutive even integers increase by 2.

EXAMPLE 2

Find 3 consecutive odd integers such that the first increased by 5 times the third is 122.

Strategy: **Same as above.**

Step 1: Represent the missing values using a variable.
Let x = the smallest number. Then,
$x + 2$ = the next odd integer, and
$x + 4$ = the third odd integer.

Step 2: Write a word equation and an algebraic equation.

The first	increased by	5 times the third	is	122.
x	+	$5(x + 4)$	=	122

Step 3: Solve the algebraic equation.
$x + 5(x + 4) = 122$
$x + 5x + 20 = 122$ Use the Distributive Property.
$6x + 20 = 122$ Combine like terms.
$6x = 102$ Subtract 20.
$x = 17$

Step 4: Find the other values.
Since the first number is 17, the next consecutive odd integer is 19, and the next is 21.

Step 5: Check your solution.

The first	increased by	5 times the third	is	122.
17	+	$5(21)$	=	122

$17 + 105 = 122$
$122 = 122$ ✔

Solution: **The three consecutive odd integers are 17, 19, and 21.**

---

③ PERIMETER PROBLEMS

EXAMPLE 3

The length of a rectangle is 5 less than 4 times the width. Find the dimensions of the rectangle if the perimeter is 230 inches.

Strategy: **Same as above.**

Step 1: Represent the missing values, the width and the length, using variables.
Let x = the shorter side, in this case the width.
Then, $4x - 5$ = the longer side, the length.

Step 2: Write a word equation that uses the meaning of perimeter (the distance around the figure) and the perimeter formula for a rectangle: $P = 2L + 2W$

Then write an algebraic equation.

2 times the length	plus	2 times the width	equals	the perimeter
$2(4x - 5)$	$+$	$2x$	$=$	230

Step 3: Solve the algebraic equation.

$$2(4x - 5) + 2x = 230$$

$8x - 10 + 2x = 230$	Use the Distributive Property.
$10x - 10 = 230$	Combine like terms.
$10x = 240$	Add 10.
$x = 24$	Divide by 10.

The width is 24 inches.

Step 4: Use the value of x (the width) to find the length.

$$\begin{aligned} 4x - 5 &= 4(24) - 5 \\ &= 96 - 5 \\ &= 91 \end{aligned}$$

The length is 91 inches.

Step 5: Check the solution.
Substitute the values for the length and width into the equation.

$$2(4(24) - 5) + 2(24) = 230$$
$$2(96 - 5) + 48 = 230$$
$$2(91) + 48 = 230 \checkmark$$

Solution: **The width is 24 inches and the length is 91 inches.**

REGENTS MATH PRACTICE

1. The larger of two numbers is 23 less than twice the smaller. If the sum of the two numbers is 70, find the two numbers.

2. Two numbers are in the ratio of 3 to 7. The sum of the numbers is 110. What are the numbers? (*Hint: Let the smaller number = 3x*)

3. One number is four times another number. If the smaller number is subtracted from the larger number, the result is the same as if the smaller number were increased by 30. What are the two numbers?

4. Two numbers have a difference of 300. One number is 7 times the other. Find the two numbers.

5. Find 3 consecutive numbers such that the sum of the second and third is 30 greater than the first.

6. Find 3 consecutive even numbers such that the sum of the first and second is 44 less than 3 times the third.

7. Find 3 consecutive odd numbers such that the sum of the first and third is 129 less than 5 times the second.

8. Each of the equal sides of an isosceles triangle is 3 inches greater than the base. If the perimeter of the triangle is 42 inches, find the length of each side.

9. When two opposite sides of a square are increased by 3 cm and the other two opposite sides are decreased by 1 cm, a rectangle with perimeter 40 results. Find the length of a side of the original square.

10. The length of a rectangle is 5 times its width. If the length is increased by 6 and the width is doubled, the new rectangle has a perimeter of 54 m. Find the dimensions of the original rectangle.

LESSON 15
EQUATIONS WITH FRACTIONS

KEY CONCEPTS YOU'LL NEED IN THIS LESSON

1. You can use prime factors to find the least common denominator (LCD) of a set of fractions:

$$\frac{3x}{6}, \frac{x}{15}$$

Prime factors of 6: 2×3 Prime factors of 15 = 3×5

LCD = $2 \times 3 \times 5 = 30$

So, both fractions can be rewritten with 30 as the denominator.

$$\frac{3x}{6} \cdot \frac{5}{5} = \frac{15x}{30} \qquad \frac{7x}{15} \cdot \frac{2}{2} = \frac{14x}{30}$$

2. To solve an equation containing fractions, first find the LCD of all the fractions in the equation. Then multiply the entire equation by the LCD and solve the equation that results.

$$\frac{a-5}{2} - \frac{a+3}{3} = 2$$

The LCD of 2 and 3 is 6.

$$6\left(\frac{(a-5)}{2} - \frac{(a+3)}{3}\right) = 2\,(6) \qquad \text{Multiply by 6, the LCD.}$$

$$\overset{3}{6}\left(\frac{(a-5)}{\underset{1}{2}}\right) - \overset{2}{6}\left(\frac{(a+3)}{\underset{1}{3}}\right) = 2\,(6) \qquad \text{Cancel where you can.}$$

$$3a - 15 - 2a - 6 = 12 \qquad \text{Use the Distributive Property.}$$
$$a - 21 = 12 \qquad \text{Combine like terms.}$$
$$a = 33 \qquad \text{Add 21.}$$

1 EQUATIONS WITH FRACTIONS

EXAMPLE 1   **Solve and check.**

$$\frac{19}{6x} - \frac{5}{6} = \frac{3}{2x}$$

Strategy: **Use Key Concepts 1 and 2.**

Step 1: Find the LCD of all the denominators:
The LCD of $6x$, 6, and $2x$ is $6x$.

Step 2: Multiply the equation by the LCD.

$$6x\left(\frac{19}{6x} - \frac{5}{6}\right) = \left(\frac{3}{2x}\right)6x$$

$$6x\left(\frac{19}{6x}\right) - 6x\left(\frac{5}{6}\right) = \left(\frac{3}{2x}\right)6x$$

Step 3: Cancel where possible and solve the equation.

$$\,^1\!6x\left(\frac{19}{6x_1}\right) - \,^{1x}\!6x\left(\frac{5}{6_1}\right) = \left(\frac{3}{2x_1}\right)\,^3\!6x$$

$$19 - 5x = 9$$
$$-5x = -10 \quad \text{Subtract 19.}$$
$$x = 2 \quad \text{Divide by -5.}$$

Step 4: Check the solution. Use the original equation.

$$\frac{19}{6x} - \frac{5}{6} = \frac{3}{2x}$$

$$\frac{19}{12} - \frac{5}{6} = \frac{3}{4} \rightarrow \frac{19}{12} - \frac{10}{12} = \frac{9}{12} \rightarrow \frac{9}{12} = \frac{9}{12} \checkmark$$

Step 5: Graph the solution:

$$-1 \quad 0 \quad 1 \quad 2 \quad 3 \quad 4 \quad 5$$

Solution: When $\frac{19}{6x} - \frac{5}{6} = \frac{3}{2x}$, $x = 2$.

---

2 SOLVING FRACTION PROBLEMS

EXAMPLE 2 Two-thirds of a number decreased by 9 is equal to $\frac{1}{6}$ of the number increased by 3. Find the number.

Strategy: Use Key Concepts 1 – 2 from Lesson 14, then Key Concept 2 from Lesson 15.

Step 1: Represent the missing number using a variable.
Let x = the number.

$\frac{2}{3}x - 9$ = two thirds of the number decreased by 9

$\frac{1}{6}x + 3$ = one sixth of the number increased by 3

Step 2: Write a word equation and an algebraic equation.

Two thirds of a number decreased by 9	is equal to	one sixth of the number increased by 3.
$\frac{2}{3}x - 9$	=	$\frac{1}{6}x + 3$

Step 3: Solve the equation.
$$\frac{2}{3}x - 9 = \frac{1}{6}x + 3$$

$$6\left(\tfrac{2}{3}x - 9\right) = \left(\tfrac{1}{6}x + 3\right)6 \qquad \text{Multiply by the LCD, 6.}$$

$$\overset{4}{\cancel{\tfrac{12}{3}}}x - 54 = \overset{1}{\cancel{\tfrac{6}{6}}}x + 18 \qquad \text{Use the Distributive Property and cancel.}$$

$$4x - 54 = x + 18$$

$$3x - 54 = 18 \qquad \text{Subtract } x.$$

$$3x = 72 \qquad \text{Add 54.}$$

$$x = 24 \qquad \text{Divide by 3.}$$

Step 4: Check the solution. Use the original equation.

$$\tfrac{2}{3}x - 9 = \tfrac{1}{6}x + 3$$

$$\tfrac{2}{3}(24) - 9 = \tfrac{1}{6}(24) + 3$$

$$16 - 9 = 4 + 3$$

$$7 = 7 \checkmark$$

Solution: When $\tfrac{2}{3}x - 9 = \tfrac{1}{6}x + 3$, $x = 24$.

EXAMPLE 3

A snack machine contains $20.80 in quarters and dimes. If there are 100 coins in all, how many of each type are there?

Strategy: **Same as above.**

Step 1: Represent the missing values using a variable.
Keep in mind that money amounts represent decimal fractions.
Let x = the number of quarters
Let $100 - x$ = the number of dimes
Then,
$0.25x$ = the value of the quarters, and
$0.10(100 - x)$ = the value of the dimes

Step 2: Write a word equation and an algebraic equation.
The value of the quarters plus   the value of the dimes   is $20.80
       $0.25x$ + $0.10(100 - x)$ = $20.80

Step 3: Solve the equation.

$$0.25x + .10(100 - x) = 20.80$$

$$100(0.25x + 0.10(100 - x)) = 20.80(100) \qquad \text{Multiply by 100, the LCD of 0.25 and 0.10.}$$

$$25x + 10(100 - x) = 2{,}080$$

$$25x + 1{,}000 - 10x = 2{,}080 \qquad \text{Use the Distributive Property.}$$

$$15x + 1{,}000 = 2{,}080 \qquad \text{Combine like terms.}$$

$$15x = 1,080 \qquad \text{Subtract 1000.}$$
$$x = 72 \qquad \text{Divide by 15.}$$

Since x represents the number of quarters, there are 72 quarters. Since $100 - x$ represents the number of dimes, there are $100 - 72$ or 28 dimes.

Step 4:   Check the solution. Use the original equation.
$$0.25x + 0.10(100 - x) = 20.80$$
$$0.25(72) + 0.10(28) = 20.80$$
$$18 + 2.80 = 20.80$$
$$20.80 = 20.80 \checkmark$$

Solution: **There are 72 quarters and 28 dimes in the snack machine.**

REGENTS MATH PRACTICE

Solve and check.

1. $\frac{x}{3} + \frac{2x}{6} = 18$

2. $\frac{5}{x} - 1 = \frac{4}{x}$

3. $\frac{19 - x}{2} + x = \frac{41 - x}{3}$

4. $4 = \frac{16}{a - 3}$

5. $\frac{16}{2b} - \frac{36}{3b} = -1$

6. One third of a number plus one fourth of the number plus one fifth of the number add to 47. Find the number.

7. One fourth of a number is 4 less than one third of the number. Find the number.

8. Find two consecutive numbers such that the difference between $\frac{1}{7}$ of the larger and $\frac{1}{9}$ of the smaller is 1.

9. After several people have used a snack machine, it has a total of $3.90 in nickels, dimes, and quarters. If the number of nickels is twice the number of dimes, and the number of quarters is $\frac{1}{4}$ the number of nickels, how many of each coin are there?

10. A driver has gone 10 miles more than half the distance she needs to travel. This is 60 miles more than $\frac{1}{7}$ of the distance she needs to go. How far does she need to travel?

LESSON ⑯
FORMULAS

KEY CONCEPTS YOU'LL NEED IN THIS LESSON

1. A **formula** is an equation that contains two or more variables.

2. A formula can be **transformed** or rewritten to solve for any variable.

3. To **transform** a formula, use the same technique you have used to solve other equations. Keep in mind that since variables represent numbers, you can apply the same operations to variables as to numbers.

   The formula for the total cost of an item that costs d dollars with $r\%$ sales tax is
   $C = d + rd$

   To transform the formula for r (that is, to solve for r, the tax rate), follow the rule for solving equations.

   $$C = d + rd$$
   $$C - d = rd \qquad \text{Subtract } d.$$
   $$\frac{C - d}{d} = r \qquad \text{Divide by } d.$$

4. To evaluate a formula for a variable, replace all other variables with their values. Then follow the order of operations.

   When $\frac{C - d}{d} = r$, find r when $C = \$129.60$ and $d = \$120$

   $$\frac{C - d}{d} = r \rightarrow \frac{129.60 - 120}{120} \rightarrow \frac{9.60}{120} \rightarrow 0.08$$

   So, in the above problem, the sales tax rate is 0.08 or 8%.

---

1 TRANSFORMING FORMULAS

EXAMPLE 1

The formula $F = \frac{9}{5}C + 32$ gives the temperature in degrees Fahrenheit for any temperature C in degrees Celsius. Transform the formula to solve for C.

Strategy: Use Key Concepts 2 and 3.

Step 1: Use the properties of equations.

$$F = \frac{9}{5}C + 32$$

$$F - 32 = \frac{9}{5}C \qquad \text{Subtract 32.}$$

$\frac{5}{9}(F - 32) = C$ Multiply by $\frac{5}{9}$, the inverse of multiplying by $\frac{9}{5}$.

Solution: $C = \frac{5}{9}(F - 32)$

---

2   EVALUATING FORMULAS

EXAMPLE 2   **The formula $i = prt$ gives the amount of interest i where p is the amount of principal, r is the interest rate, and t is the time in years. Find p when i = \$1,008, r = 9% (0.09 as a decimal), and t = 4 years.**

Strategy: **Use Key Concepts 1 and 2.**

Step 1:   Transform the formula so that the variable p is alone on one side of the equals sign.

$i = prt$

$\frac{i}{rt} = p$ Divide each side of the equation by rt.

Step 2:   Evaluate the formula for the given values of the variables.

$\frac{i}{rt} = p \rightarrow \frac{1{,}008}{0.09(4)} \rightarrow \frac{1{,}008}{0.36} = 2{,}800$

Solution: **The value of the principal p is \$2,800.**

REGENTS MATH PRACTICE

Transform the formula for the given variable.

1. $A = \pi r^2$ for r

2. $P = 2l + 2w$ for w

3. $A = \dfrac{h(b_1 + b_2)}{2}$ for b_1

4. $s = \dfrac{1}{2}at^2$ for a

5. $V = \dfrac{1}{3}\pi r^2 h$ for r

6. $a^2 + b^2 = c^2$ for b

Evaluate each formula.

7.   If $V = lwh$, find w when $V = 1152$, $l = 16$, and $h = 9$.

8.   If $K = mv^2$, find m when $K = 128$ and $v = 4$.

9.   If $F = \dfrac{9}{5}C + 32$, find C when $F = 50$.

10.   If $s = \dfrac{n}{2}(a + l)$, find a when $s = 160$, $n = 20$, and $l = 6$

LESSON 17
INEQUALITIES

KEY CONCEPTS YOU'LL NEED IN THIS LESSON

1. An **inequality** can be represented by one of the following symbols:

   <   "is less than"
   >   "is greater than"
   ≤   "is less than or equal to"
   ≥   "is greater than or equal to"

2. Solve an inequality the same way you solve an equation.

   However, when you multiply or divide by a NEGATIVE number, <u>reverse</u> the direction of the inequality symbol.

   $$x + 3 < 7 \qquad \text{But:} \qquad -3x + 2 \geq 23$$
   $$\underline{-3 \quad -3} \qquad\qquad \underline{\quad -2 \quad -2}$$
   $$x < 4 \qquad\qquad\qquad -3x \geq 21$$
   $$\frac{-3x}{-3} \leq \frac{21}{-3}$$

   (*division by a NEGATIVE*—reverse the inequality symbol)

   $$x \leq -7$$

3. You can graph the solution set of an inequality on a number line:

   $$-3x + 2 \geq 23$$
   $$x \leq -7$$

   - The filled-in circle at -7 indicates that -7 is part of the solution set.
   - The heavy line with the arrow to the left indicates that all numbers less than -7 are also solutions to the inequality.

4. Other types of inequalities can be solved and graphed.

   a. $-1 \leq x < 4$

   Think of $-1 \leq x < 4$ as the **conjunction** of two inequalities: $(-1 \leq x)$ and $(x < 4)$:
   The solution set consists of all numbers—
        equal to or greater than -1, AND less than 4.

   - The filled-in circle at -1 shows that -1 is part of the solution set.
   - The open circle at 4 shows that the solution set does **not** include 4.

b. $(x < -2) \lor (x \geq 1)$

Think of $(x < -2) \lor (x \geq 1)$ as a **disjunction**. (Remember, the $\lor$ stands for "or.")

The solution consists of all numbers—
       less than -2, OR
       equal to or greater than 1
       OR BOTH.

1   SOLVING AND GRAPHING INEQUALITIES

EXAMPLE 1

Solve, check, and graph the solution set.
$-3x + 8 \geq 2$

Strategy: **Use Key Concepts 2 and 3.**

Step 1:   Solve as an equation.

$$-3x + 8 \geq 2$$
$$\underline{\quad - 8 \quad - 8} \qquad \text{Subtract 8.}$$
$$-3x \geq -6$$
$$\frac{-3x}{-3} \leq \frac{-6}{-3} \qquad \text{Divide by -3. Reverse the direction of the inequality symbol.}$$
$$x \leq 2$$

Step 2:   Check the solution. Pick any value in the solution set (that is, any value less than or equal to 2). Test it in the original inequality. Try 0.

$$-3x + 8 \geq 2$$
$$-3(0) + 8 \geq 2$$
$$8 \geq 2 ✔ \qquad \text{The solution checks.}$$

Step 3:   Graph the solution.

Solution: **When $-3x + 8 \geq 2$, x can be any value less than or equal to 2.**

EXAMPLE 2

Graph the solution set of each inequality.
a. $-4 \leq x \leq 0$ b. $(x < -5) \vee (x \geq -1)$

Strategy: **Use Key Concept 4.**

Step 1:
a. $-4 \leq x \leq 0$
Recognize that this inequality is a **conjunction**. The solution set is between -4 and 0 and includes both -4 and 0.

b. $(x < -5) \vee (x \geq -1)$
Recognize that this inequality is a **disjunction**. The solution set is less than -5 or greater than -1. It also includes -1.

-4 -3 -2 -1 0 1 2

-6 -5 -4 -3 -2 -1 0 1

---

2 SOLVING PROBLEMS USING INEQUALITIES

EXAMPLE 3

Jena's Aunt Marilyn is 3 years older than 3 times Jena's age. Twice the sum of their ages is at most 78. Find the greatest possible age for both of them.

Strategy: **Use Key Concepts 1, 2, 3, and 4 from Lesson 13, applying them to inequalities.**

Step 1:
Represent the missing values using a variable.
Let x = Jena's age, then
Let $3x + 3$ = her Aunt Marilyn's age

Step 2:
Write a word inequality to represent the information in the problem. Then write an algebraic inequality from the word inequality.

Twice the sum of their ages	is at most	78
$2(x + 3x + 3)$	$\leq$	78

Step 3:
Solve the inequality.
$2(x + 3x + 3) \leq 78$
$2x + 6x + 6 \leq 78$ Use the Distributive Property.
$8x + 6 \leq 78$ Combine like terms.
$8x \leq 72$ Subtract 6.
$x \leq 9$ Divide by 8.

So, Jena's age is 9 or less.
Her Aunt Marilyn's age is $3(9) + 3$. She must be 30 or less.

Step 4:   Check the solution.
$$2(9 + 30) \le 78$$
$$2(39) \le 78$$
$$78 \le 78 \checkmark$$

Solution: **The greatest possible ages are Jena: 9, Marilyn: 30.**

REGENTS MATH PRACTICE

Solve each inequality. Graph the solution.

1. $4x - 9 > 23$

    6   7   8   9   10   11   12

2. $-6m \le 24$

    -6   -7   -4   -3   -2   -1   0

3. $\frac{r}{5} - 2 < 4$

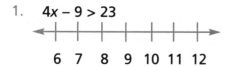

    27   28   29   30   31   32   33

4. $-10 \ge -2t + 2$

    5   6   7   8   9   10   11

5. $3x + 7 > 22$

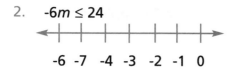

    4   5   6   7   8   9   10

6. $\frac{-y}{9} \le -3$

    26   27   28   29   30   31   32

7. $3r + 1 < 4r + 7$

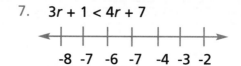

    -8 -7 -6 -7 -4 -3 -2

8.   Five times a number x decreased by 7 is no more than 33. Find the solution set.

9.   A monthly transit pass costs $55. The regular price of each ride is $1.60. What is the least number of rides for which it makes sense to buy the monthly pass? Explain how you decided.

10.   A taxi company charges $1.75 for the first $\frac{1}{4}$ mile and $.30 for each additional $\frac{1}{4}$ mile. What is the greatest whole number of miles you can travel and pay less than $15.00? Explain the method you used.

LESSON (18)
QUADRATIC EQUATIONS

KEY CONCEPTS YOU'LL NEED IN THIS LESSON

1. A **quadratic equation** is an equation in which the greatest power of a variable is 2.

2. A quadratic equation is said to be in **standard form** when one side (usually the right side) is 0.

Quadratic Equation	Same Equation in Standard Form
$x^2 - 4x = 5$	$x^2 - 4x - 5 = 0$
$2x^2 = 72$	$2x^2 - 72 = 0$
$x^2 - 3x - 10 = 0$	$x^2 - 3x - 10 = 0$ (same as original)

3. **To solve a quadratic equation**, factor the left side of the equation. The result is a multiplication sentence in which the product is 0. When this occurs, at least one of the factors must be 0.

$$x^2 + x - 30 = 0 \quad \text{Equation in standard form}$$
$$(x + 6)(x - 5) = 0 \quad \text{Factor the left side.}$$
$$x + 6 = 0 \quad | \quad x - 5 = 0 \quad \text{Set each factor equal to 0.}$$
$$x = -6 \quad | \quad x = 5 \quad \text{Solve each equation for } x.$$

When $x^2 + x - 30 = 0$, $x = -6$ and $x = 5$ are the **roots** (solutions) of the equation.

Check the solution by substituting each root into the original equation.

$\underline{x = -6}$
$(-6)^2 + (-6) - 30 = 0?$
$36 - 6 - 30 = 0$
$0 = 0$ ✔

$\underline{x = 5}$
$5^2 + 5 - 30 = 0?$
$25 + 5 - 30 = 0$
$0 = 0$ ✔

1 SOLVING QUADRATIC EQUATIONS

EXAMPLE 1

Solve and check: $x^2 - 4x = 21$

Strategy: **Use Key Concepts 1 and 2.**

Step 1: Write the equation in standard form.
$x^2 - 4x - 21 = 0$

Step 2: Factor the left side and solve.
$x^2 - 4x - 21 = 0$
$(x - 7)(x + 3) = 0$
$x - 7 = 0 \quad | \quad x + 3 = 0$
$x = 7 \quad | \quad x = -3$

Step 3: Check:

$$\underline{x = 7}$$
$7^2 - 4(7) - 21 = 0\ ?$
$49 - 28 - 21 = 0$
$0 = 0\ ✔$

$$\underline{x = \text{-}3}$$
$(\text{-}3)^2 - 4(\text{-}3) - 21 = 0\ ?$
$9 + 12 - 21 = 0$
$0 = 0\ ✔$

Solution: **The roots of the equation $x^2 - 4x - 21 = 0$ are $x = 7$ and $x = \text{-}3$.**

EXAMPLE 2 | **Solve and check: $x^2 - 7x = 0$**

Strategy: **Same as above.**

Step 1: Factor the left side, using the common factor, x.
$x^2 - 7x = 0$
$x(x - 7) = 0$
$x = 0\ \bigg|\ x - 7 = 0$
$\qquad\qquad x = 7$

Step 2: Check:

$$\underline{x = 0}$$
$0^2 - 7(0) = 0\ ?$
$0 = 0\ ✔$

$$\underline{x = 7}$$
$7^2 - 7(7) = 0\ ?$
$0 = 0\ ✔$

Solution: **The roots of the equation $x^2 - 7x = 0$ are $x = 0$ and $x = 7$.**

EXAMPLE 3 | **Solve and check: $3x^2 = 15$**

Strategy: **Same as above.**

Step 1: Simplify the equation.

$$\frac{3x^2}{3} = \frac{15}{3}$$

$x^2 = 5$

Step 2: Find the two roots and check.
$x^2 = 5$
$x = \sqrt{5}$ or $x = \text{-}\sqrt{5}$
Both roots are irrational numbers. Leave them in radical form.

Step 3: Check:

$$\underline{x = \sqrt{5}}$$
$3(\sqrt{5})^2 = 15?$
$3(5) = 15$
$15 = 15\ ✔$

$$\underline{x = \text{-}\sqrt{5}}$$
$3(\text{-}\sqrt{5})^2 = 15$
$3(5) = 15$
$15 = 15\ ✔$

Solution: **The roots of the equation $3x^2 = 15$ are $x = \sqrt{5}$ and $x = \text{-}\sqrt{5}$.**

2 SOLVING PROBLEMS WITH QUADRATIC EQUATIONS

EXAMPLE 4

Find three consecutive positive integers such that the square of the first plus the second is 3 more than 8 times the third.

Strategy: **Use Key Concepts 1 – 4 from Lesson 14.**

Step 1: Define the variables.
Let x = the first number
$x + 1$ = the second number
$x + 2$ = the third number

Step 2: Write a word equation and an algebraic equation to represent the relationships in the problem. Then solve the algebraic equation.

The square of the first	plus	the second	is	3 more than	8 times the third.
x^2	$+$	$(x + 1)$	$=$	$3 +$	$8(x + 2)$

$$x^2 + (x + 1) = 8(x + 2) + 3$$
$$x^2 + x + 1 = 8x + 16 + 3 \qquad \text{Use the Distributive Property.}$$
$$x^2 + x + 1 = 8x + 19 \qquad \text{Combine like terms.}$$
$$x^2 + 1 = 7x + 19 \qquad \text{Subtract } x.$$
$$x^2 = 7x + 18 \qquad \text{Subtract 1.}$$
$$x^2 - 7x - 18 = 0 \qquad \text{Write in standard form.}$$
$$(x + 2)(x - 9) = 0 \qquad \text{Factor the left side.}$$

$x + 2 = 0 \quad | \quad x - 9 = 0 \qquad$ Set each factor equal to 0.
$\quad\quad x = -2 \quad | \quad\quad x = 9 \qquad$ Solve.

Reject -2 as a solution because the problem states that the integers are positive.

Solution: **The numbers are 9, 10, and 11.**

EXAMPLE 5

The length of a rectangle is twice its width. If the length is increased by 2 and the width is decreased by 1, the new rectangle has an area of 30 square ft. Find the dimensions of the original rectangle.

Strategy: **Same as Example 4**

Step 1: Define the variables.
Let x = the width of the original rectangle.
$2x$ = the length of the original rectangle
$2x + 2$ = length of new rectangle
$x - 1$ = width of new rectangle

Step 2:   Use a word equation and an algebraic equation.

length $\times$ width = area

$$(2x + 2)(x - 1) = 30$$

$2x^2 - 2 = 30$	Multiply the binomials.
$2x^2 - 32 = 0$	Write in standard form.
$x^2 - 16 = 0$	Divide by 2.
$(x + 4)(x - 4) = 0$	Factor the left side.
$x + 4 = 0 \quad | \quad x - 4 = 0$ S	et each factor equal to 0.
$x = -4 \quad | \quad x = 4$	Solve.

Reject -4, because a rectangle cannot have a dimension that is a negative integer.

Solution: **The original width x of the rectangle was 4 ft. The original length was 8 ft.**

REGENTS MATH PRACTICE

In problems 1–5, solve and check.

1. $x^2 - 6x = 7$

2. $x^2 + 8x = 20$

3. $x^2 - 16 = 6x$

4. $x(x + 5) = 14$

5. $x^2 - 9x + 20 = 0$

6. Find two consecutive integers such that the sum of their squares is 113. Explain how you decided which root of the quadratic equation to use.

7. The length of a rectangle is 5 more than its width. If its area is 414 square feet, find the dimensions of the rectangle.

8. When one pair of opposite sides of a square are increased by 3 and the other pair are decreased by 1, the area of the resulting rectangle is 77 square meters. Find the length of a side of the original square.

9. When the square of a positive number is decreased by 6 times the number, the result is 27. Find the number.

10. The base of a triangle measures 4 cm less than the altitude. If the area is 30 cm², find the dimensions of the triangle.

UNIT ③ REVIEW

In questions 1–5, find and graph the solution.

1. $8 - 5x = 12 - 3x$

   -4 -3 -2 -1 0 1 2

2. $13 - 6(x + 2) = -5x - 4$

   2 3 4 5 6 7 8

3. $2 + \frac{1}{x} = \frac{5}{2}$

   -1 0 1 2 3 4 5

4. $-3t + 7 \, '' \, -8$

   -1 0 1 2 3 4 5

5. $12n - 3 > 13n$

   -3 -2 -1 0 1 2 3

6. Find 3 consecutive positive odd integers such that the sum of the second and third is 23 greater than the first.

7. Each of the two equal sides of an isosceles triangle is 6 inches longer than the base. The perimeter of the triangle is 30 inches. Find the lengths of the sides.

8. One half of a number is 6 more than one fifth of the number. Find the number.

9. Katie and her dog standing on a scale together weigh no more than 120 pounds. Katie weighs 12 pounds more than her dog. What is the most her dog can weigh?

10. The difference between 7 times a number x and 38 is at least 4. Find the solution set.

Solve and check.

11. $x^2 + 2x - 15 = 0$

12. $3y^2 - 12 = 0$

13. $3x^2 = 75$

14. $w^2 = 8w$

15. $x^2 = x + 30$

16. $2x^2 - x = 10$

17. The length of a rectangle is 2 less than twice the width. If the area is 144 cm², find the dimensions of the rectangle.

LESSON 19
ANGLES AND ANGLE PAIRS

KEY CONCEPTS YOU'LL NEED IN THIS LESSON

1. Angles are classified by their measures.

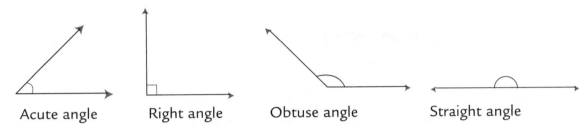

Acute angle   Right angle   Obtuse angle   Straight angle

2. Angles with the same measure are **congruent**.

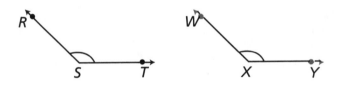

$\angle RST \cong \angle WXY$
Read "Angle *RST* is congruent to angle *WXY*."

3. **Complementary angles** are two angles for which the sum is 90°.
    They may or may not be adjacent.

4. **Supplementary angles** are two angles for which the sum is 180°.
    They may or may not be adjacent.

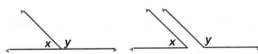

5. **Vertical angles** are formed by two intersecting lines.
    $\angle ROT$ and $\angle SOU$ are vertical angles.
    $\angle ROS$ and $\angle TOU$ are also a vertical pair.
    Vertical angles are congruent.

1 ANGLE CLASSIFICATION

EXAMPLE 1

A pair of complementary angles are congruent.
a. Classify the angles according to their measure.
b. Find the measure of each angle.

Strategy: **Use Key Concepts 1, 2, and 3.**

Step 1: Classify the angles.
Since the angles are complementary, their sum is 90°. Therefore, they must both be acute angles.

Step 2: Find the measure of each angle.
Since the angles are congruent and their sum is 90°, the measure of each angle must be $\frac{90}{2}$ or 45°.

Solution: **If complementary angles are congruent, they are acute and the measure of each must be 45°.**

2 ANGLE PAIRS

EXAMPLE 2

The measures of two supplementary angles are in the ratio of 3:2. Find the measure of each angle.

Strategy: **Use Key Concept 4.**

Step 1: Use a variable to represent the two angles. Since the angles are in the ratio 3:2, let
$3x$ = the larger angle and $2x$ = the smaller angle.

Step 2: Write and solve an equation that represents the relationship of the angles. Since they are supplementary, their sum must be 180°.
$$3x + 2x = 180$$
$$5x = 180$$
$$x = 36, \quad \text{so } 3x = 108 \text{ and } 2x = 72$$

Step 3: Check your solution.
Are the angles in the ratio 3:2? $\frac{108}{72} = \frac{3}{2}$ ✔
Are the angles supplementary? $108 + 72 = 180$ ✔

Solution: **If two angles are supplementary and in the ratio 3:2, their measures are 108° and 72°.**

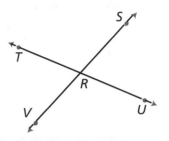

EXAMPLE 3

$\overleftrightarrow{TU}$ and $\overleftrightarrow{SV}$ intersect at R. If m∠TRS (read as "the measure of angle TRS") is 115°, find the measures of ∠VRU, ∠TRV, and ∠SRU.

Strategy: Use Key Concept 5 and then 4.

Step 1: Find the measure of ∠VRU.
Since ∠TRS and ∠VRU are vertical angles, they are congruent.
The measure of ∠VRU must be 115°.

Step 2: Find the measure of ∠TRV.
Since ∠TRS and ∠TRV are supplementary, their sum must be 180°.
Since 180 – 115 = 65, m∠TRV must be 65°.

Step 3: Find the measure of ∠SRU.
Since ∠TRV and ∠SRU are vertical angles, they are congruent.
The measure of ∠SRU must be 65°.

Solution: If m∠TRS = 115°, then m∠VRU = 115°, m∠TRV = 65°, and m∠SRU = 65°.

EXAMPLE 4

In the figure above, if m∠TRV = 2x + 15 and m∠SRU = 3x – 9, find the measures of each of the four angles.

Strategy: Use Key Concept 5 and then 4.

Step 1: Since vertical angles are congruent, write and solve an equation from the given information.
$$2x + 15 = 3x - 9$$
$$2x + 24 = 3x$$
$$24 = x$$

Step 2: Use the value of x to find the measures of ∠TRV and ∠SRU.
$$\begin{aligned} m\angle TRV &= 2x + 15 & m\angle TRS &= 3x - 9 \\ &= 2(24) + 15 & &= 3(24) - 9 \\ &= 63° & &= 63° \end{aligned}$$

Step 3: Find the measure of ∠VRU. Use the fact that ∠TRV and ∠VRU are supplementary.
$$m\angle VRU = 180 - 63 = 117°$$

Step 4: Find the measure of ∠TRS. Use the fact that ∠TRS and ∠VRU are vertical angles.
$$m\angle TRS = m\angle VRU = 117°$$

Solution: If $m\angle TRV = 2x + 15$ and $m\angle SRU = 3x - 9$, then the angles have the following measures: $m\angle TRV = 63°$, $m\angle SRU = 63°$, $m\angle VRU = 117°$, and $m\angle TRS = 117°$.

REGENTS MATH PRACTICE

1. What is an expression for an angle that is complementary to an angle that measures $x°$?
    a. $x + 90$
    b. $x - 90$
    c. $90 - x$
    d. $\frac{90}{x}$

2. The difference between the supplement and complement of an acute angle is
    f. an acute angle
    g. a right angle
    h. an obtuse angle
    j. a straight angle

    Explain how you chose the correct answer to the question.

3. Two complementary angles are in the ratio 5:1. What is the measure of the smaller angle?
    a. 5°
    b. 15°
    c. 20°
    d. 75°

4. If a pair of angles are vertical, they cannot be
    f. complementary
    g. congruent
    h. supplementary
    j. straight angles

5. The measure of the supplement of an angle is 72° greater than the angle. What is the measure of the angle?
    a. 18°
    b. 54°
    c. 108°
    d. 162°

6. The complement of angle x has a measure 40° greater than angle x. What is the supplement of angle x?
    f. 50°
    g. 65°
    h. 125°
    j. 155°

    Describe the steps you used to find the supplement of angle x.

    In the figure at the right, $m\angle XYV$ is $6x + 15$. The measure of $\angle WYZ$ is $7x - 5$.

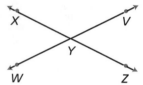

7. What is the value of x?
    a. 15°
    b. 20°
    c. 25°
    d. 30°

8. What is the measure of $\angle WYZ$?
    f. 110°
    g. 120°
    h. 135°
    j. 145°

9. What is the measure of $\angle XYW$?
    a. 20°
    b. 45°
    c. 70°
    d. 75°

10. If $\angle XYV$ and $\angle XYW$ were congruent, which statement would be true?
    f. All four vertical angles would be right angles.
    g. There would be exactly one pair of right angles.
    h. $m\angle XYV$ would be greater than $m\angle WYZ$.
    j. Two angles would be greater than 90° and two would be less than 90°.

LESSON ⟨20⟩ PERPENDICULAR AND PARALLEL LINES

KEY CONCEPTS YOU'LL NEED IN THIS LESSON

1. **Perpendicular lines** intersect to form 4 right angles.

2. A **perpendicular bisector** of a line segment can be a line, a segment, or a ray. It is perpendicular to the segment at its midpoint.

3. **Parallel lines** are lines in the same plane that do not intersect.

    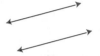

    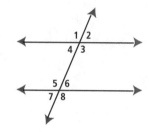

4. If two parallel lines are cut by a third line (a **transversal**), then the following pairs of congruent angles are formed:

    - **Alternate interior angles**: angles that are inside the parallel lines on opposite sides of the transversal: ∠3 and ∠5, ∠4 and ∠6

    - **Corresponding angles**: angles that are either above or below the parallel lines on the same side of the transversal: ∠1 and ∠5, ∠2 and ∠6, ∠3 and ∠8, ∠4 and ∠7

    - **Alternate exterior angles**: angles that are outside the parallel lines on opposite sides of the transversal: ∠1 and ∠8, ∠2 and ∠7

5. When two parallel lines are cut by a transversal, **interior angles on the same side of the transversal** are supplementary: ∠4 and ∠5 above, ∠3 and ∠6 above

> ***Keep in mind:***
>
> *The converse of each of the above statements is also true.*
>
> *If two lines are cut by a transversal creating congruent alternate interior angles, the lines are parallel.*
>
> *If two lines are cut by a transversal creating congruent corresponding angles, the lines are parallel.*
>
> *If two lines are cut by a transversal creating congruent alternate exterior angles, the lines are parallel.*
>
> *If two lines are cut by a transversal creating supplementary interior angles on the same side of the transversal, the lines are congruent.*

1 PERPENDICULAR LINES

EXAMPLE 1

$\overline{PQ}$ is the perpendicular bisector of $\overline{RS}$ at O.
Find the value of x.
Find the length of $\overline{RS}$.

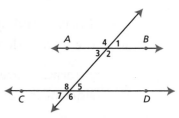

Strategy: Use Key Concepts 1 and 2.

Step 1: Write and solve an equation for x.
$$3x - 7 = 2x + 2$$
$$x - 7 = 2$$
$$x = 9$$

Step 2: Find the length of either $\overline{RO}$ or $\overline{OS}$.
RO: $3x - 7$
$3(9) - 7 = 20$
So, $RS = 2(20) = 40$ units

Solution: $x = 9$ and $RS = 40$ units

2 PARALLEL LINES

EXAMPLE 2

In the figure at the right, $\overleftrightarrow{AB}$ and $\overleftrightarrow{CD}$ are
parallel. If the measure of $\angle 3$ is $40°$, find the
measures of the other angles.

Strategy: Use Key Concept 4.

Step 1: Use the statements about parallel lines.
By vertical angles ($\angle 1$ and $\angle 3$), $m\angle 1 = 40°$.
By supplementary angles ($\angle 2$ and $\angle 3$), $m\angle 2 = 180 - 40 = 140°$.
By supplementary angles ($\angle 3$ and $\angle 4$), $m\angle 4 = 180 - 40 = 140°$.
By alternate interior angles ($\angle 3$ and $\angle 5$), $m\angle 5 = 40°$.
By supplementary angles ($\angle 5$ and $\angle 6$), $m\angle 6 = 140°$.
By corresponding angles ($\angle 3$ and $\angle 7$), $m\angle 7 = 40°$.
By supplementary angles ($\angle 3$ and $\angle 8$), $m 8 = 140°$.

Solution: The measures of angles 1, 3, 5, and 7 are all $40°$.
The measures of angles 2, 4, 6, and 8 are all $140°$.

$\boxed{\textbf{EXAMPLE 3}}$ | In the figure in example 2, if $m\angle 3 = 2x + 15$ and $m\angle 6 = 6x + 5$, find the measures of the other angles.

Strategy: Use Key Concept 5.

Step 1: Write and solve an equation for x.

$$(2x + 15) + (6x + 5) = 180$$
$$8x + 20 = 180$$
$$8x = 160$$
$$x = 20$$

So, $m\angle 3 = 2(20) + 15 = 55°$ and $m\angle 6 = 6(20) + 5 = 125°$.

Step 2: Find the measures of the other angles.
The measures of angles 1, 5, and 7 are all 55°.
The measures of angles 2, 4, and 8 are all 125°.

Solution: **Each acute angle has a measure of 55°.**
Each obtuse angle has a measure of 125°.

REGENTS MATH PRACTICE

$\overrightarrow{LR}$ is the perpendicular bisector of $\overline{MN}$ at O, $MO = 4x - 6$ and $ON = 3x + 4$.

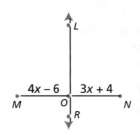

1. Name two congruent line segments.

2. Name four right angles.

3. Find the value of x.

4. Find the length of MN.

$\overleftrightarrow{DE}$ and $\overleftrightarrow{GJ}$ are parallel. $\overleftrightarrow{KL}$ is a transversal that cuts both lines.

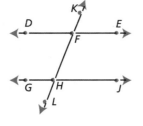

5. If $m\angle KFE$ is $4x$ and $m\angle GHL = 6x - 30$,
   a. Find the value of x.
   b. Find $m\angle KFE$.

6. If $m\angle DFH = 5x + 8$ and $m\angle FHJ = 8x - 16$,
   a. Find the value of x.
   b. Find $m\angle FHJ$.

7. If the ratio of $m\angle EFH$ to $m\angle FHJ$ is 7:2,
   a. Find the measure of $\angle EFH$.
   b. Find the measure of $\angle FHJ$.

8. Two parallel lines are cut by a transversal. If the measures of two interior angles on the same side of the transversal are represented by $6x$ and $3x$, find the measure of the larger angle. Explain your solution method.

9. Two parallel lines are cut by a transversal. If a pair of vertical angles formed by the transversal are supplementary, what can you tell about the transversal? Explain how you know.

10. Two parallel lines are cut by a transversal. If a pair of alternate interior angles are complementary, what can you tell about the angle that the transversal makes with the parallel lines?

LESSON 21
POLYGONS

KEY CONCEPTS YOU'LL NEED IN THIS LESSON

1. A **polygon** is a simple closed figure. It consists only of line segments. The point where line segments meet is called a **vertex**.

2. Specially named polygons include:

Name	Number of sides
Triangle	3
Quadrilateral	4
Pentagon	5
Hexagon	6
Heptagon	7
Octagon	8
Nonagon	9
Decagon	10
n-gon (general polygon)	*n*

3. A polygon is **convex** if each of its interior angles measures less than 180°.

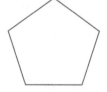

4. A regular polygon is both **equilateral** (all sides congruent) and **equiangular** (all angles congruent).

5. The sum of the measures of the **interior angles** of a polygon with *n* sides is $180(n - 2)°$.

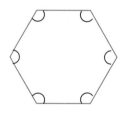

6. The sum of the measures of the **exterior angles** of a polygon with *n* sides is 360°.

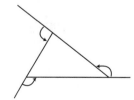

1 REGULAR POLYGONS

EXAMPLE 1

Find the number of degrees in the measure of each interior angle and each exterior angle of a regular hexagon.

Strategy: **Use Key Concepts 1, 4, 5, and 6.**

Step 1: Find the number of degrees in the sum of all the interior angles.
Total number of degrees = $180(n - 2)$
$$= 180(6 - 2) = 180(4) = 720$$

So, the number of degrees in the sum of the interior angles of a regular hexagon is 720°

Step 2: Find the number of degrees in the measure of each interior angle. A hexagon has 6 interior angles.
$720 \div 6 = 120$

So, each interior angle of a regular hexagon has a measure of 120°.

Step 3: Find the measure of each exterior angle.
The total number of degrees in all the exterior angles is 360.
$360 \div 6 = 60$.

So, each exterior angle measures 60°.

Solution: **In a regular hexagon, each interior angle has a measure of 120°. Each exterior angle has a measure of 60°.**

Note that in any polygon, the interior angle and exterior angle at every vertex will be supplementary.

EXAMPLE 2

Find the number of sides in a regular polygon if
a) the measure of each interior angle is 144°.
b) the measure of each exterior angle is 24°.
c) the sum of the measures of all the interior angles is 1,080°.

Strategy: **Use Key Concepts 5 and 6 and work backward from Example 1.**

Step 1: Find the number of sides in the polygon if the measure of each interior angle is 144°.
Use the fact that at each vertex, the interior and exterior angles are supplementary. Find the measure of an exterior angle.
$180 - 144 = 36$
Then use the fact that the sum of the exterior angles is 360°.
$360 \div 36 = 10$
So, a regular polygon whose interior angles each measure 144° has 10 sides.

Step 2: Find the number of sides if each exterior angle is 24°.
Divide 360 ÷ 24 to find the number of exterior angles.
360 ÷ 24 = 15, the number of angles and sides.
So, a regular polygon in which each exterior angle is 24° has 15 sides.

Step 3: Find the number of sides if the sum of the interior angles is 1,080°.
Use the relationship between the number of sides and the sum of the measures of the interior angles.

$180(n - 2) = 1,080$
$180n - 360 = 1,080$
$180n = 1,440$
$n = 8$

So, a regular polygon with an interior angle sum of 1,080° has 8 sides.

---

2   POLYGONS

EXAMPLE 3 **Find the number of sides of a polygon whose interior angle measures have a sum of 2520. What can you tell about the sum of the exterior angles?**

Strategy: **Use Key Concept 5 and 6.**

Step 1: Find the number of sides in the polygon.
Use the relationship: sum of measures of interior angles = $180(n - 2)$ where n is the number of sides.

$2520 = 180(n - 2)$
$2520 = 180n - 360$
$2880 = 180n$
$16 = n$

Step 2: The sum of the measures of the exterior angles of any polygon is 360°.
So, the sum of the measures of this polygon is 360°.

Solution: **The polygon has 16 sides. The sum of the exterior angles is 360°.**

REGENTS MATH PRACTICE

1. What can you tell about a polygon if the sum of the measures of the interior angles is 900°?

    1) The polygon is a regular polygon.
    2) The polygon is convex.
    3) The polygon is a heptagon.
    4) The sum of the exterior angles is 360°.

    a. 1 only   b. 1 and 3 only
    c. 3 only   d. 3 and 4 only

2. Find the sum of the measures of the interior angles of a nonagon (a 9-sided polygon).

3. Find the sum of the measures of the exterior angles of a decagon.

4. In a regular polygon, the measure of each exterior angle is 15°. Find the number of sides on the polygon.

5. How much greater is the measure of an interior angle than an exterior angle of a regular pentagon?

6. The ratio of the measures of an interior angle to an exterior angle of a regular polygon is 3:1. Find the number of sides in the polygon. Explain how you solved the problem.

7. Describe what happens to the measure of each exterior angle and each interior angle of a regular polygon as the number of sides of the polygon increases.

8. If the sum of the measures of the interior angles of a regular polygon increases from 1,800° to 2,880°, how many sides have been added to the polygon? Explain how you decided.

9. What is the sum of the measures of the interior angles of a regular polygon if each exterior angle has a measure of 72°? Name the polygon.

10. How much greater is the measure of an exterior angle of a regular quadrilateral than a regular hexagon?

LESSON ㉒ TRIANGLES

KEY CONCEPTS YOU'LL NEED IN THIS LESSON

1. Triangles can be classified according to their sides or their angles.

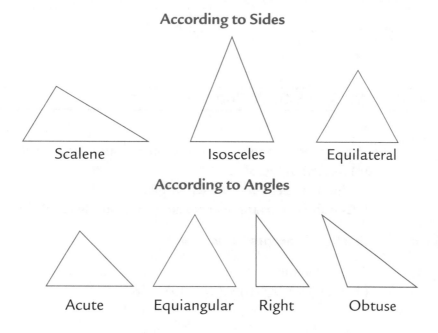

According to Sides

Scalene   Isosceles   Equilateral

According to Angles

Acute   Equiangular   Right   Obtuse

2. The sum of the measures of the angles of any triangle is 180°.

3. The measure of an exterior angle of a triangle is equal to the sum of the measures of the two remote interior angles.

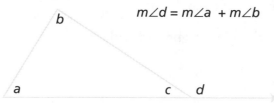

$$m\angle d = m\angle a + m\angle b$$

4. In an isosceles triangle, two angles are equal in measure and the sides opposite the angles are equal in measure.

5. The sum of the lengths of any two sides of a triangle must be greater than the length of the third side.

6. A pair of triangles can be shown to be congruent by showing that any of the following statements is true:

   a) Two sides and the angle between them of one triangle are congruent respectively to two sides and the angle between them of another triangle.

b) Two angles and the side between them of one triangle are congruent respectively to two angles and the side between them of another triangle.

c) Three sides of one triangle are congruent respectively to three sides of another triangle.

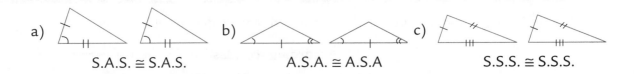

a) S.A.S. ≅ S.A.S.   b) A.S.A. ≅ A.S.A   c) S.S.S. ≅ S.S.S.

---

1 ANGLES AND SIDES OF A TRIANGLE

EXAMPLE 1

The degree measures of a triangle are $4x + 10$, $3x + 5$, and $2x - 15$.
a. Find the value of x.
b. Find the measure of each angle.
c. Classify the triangle according to its angles and sides.

Strategy: **Use Key Concepts 2 and then 1.**

Step 1: Find the value of x.
$$(4x + 10) + (3x + 5) + (2x - 15) = 180$$
$$9x = 180$$
$$x = 20$$

Step 2: Find the measure of each angle.
$$4(20) + 10 = 90° \qquad 3(20) + 5 = 65° \qquad 2(20) - 15 = 25°$$
$$90 + 65 + 25 = 180°$$

Step 3: Classify the triangle.

Solution: **The triangle is right and scalene.**

EXAMPLE 2

In an isosceles triangle, one exterior angle at the base measures $112°$. Find the measure of the vertex angle.

Strategy: **Use Key Concepts 1, 4, and 3.**

Step 1: Sketch a diagram of the triangle.

Step 2: Find the measure of angles x and y.
$$x + 112 = 180$$
$x = 68$, so $m\angle x = 68°$ and $m\angle y = 68°$
because base angles are equal.

z

$y \qquad x \quad 112°$

Step 3: Find the measure of the vertex angle.

$z = 180 - (68 + 68)$

$z = 44$

Solution: **The measure of the vertex angle, $\angle z$, is 44°.**

EXAMPLE 3 **Two sides of a triangle measure 3 cm and 8 cm. Find all possible lengths of the third side.**

Strategy: **Use Key Concept 5.**

Step 1: Define a variable. Let x = the length of the third side.

Step 2: Consider the two possibilities:
a) The side of length 8 is the longest side.
b) The side of length x is the longest side.

a) If 8 is the longest side, then   b) If x is the longest side, then
   $x + 3 > 8$ $3 + 8 > x$
   $x > 5$ $11 > x$ or $x < 11$

So, as an inequality, $5 < x < 11$.

Solution: **If only whole number lengths are considered, the third side of the triangle can be 6, 7, 8, 9, or 10 cm long.**

---

2 CONGRUENT TRIANGLES

EXAMPLE 4 **Explain how you would demonstrate that each pair of triangles are congruent.**

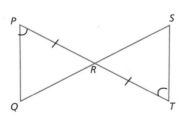

a

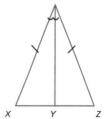

b

Strategy: **Use Key Concept 6.**

Step 1: Examine figure a. One side and one angle of each triangle are labeled congruent.

Also, $\angle PRQ \cong \angle TRS$ since they are vertical angles.
So, triangle $PRQ \cong$ triangle RST by A.S.A $\cong$ A.S.A.

Step 2: Examine figure b. One side and one angle of each triangle are labeled congruent.
Also, side WY is common to both triangles.
So, triangle $WXY \cong$ triangle WZY by S.A.S. $\cong$ S.A.S.

REGENTS MATH PRACTICE

1. The ratio of the angle measures of a triangle are 6:5:4.
   a. Find the measure of each angle.
   b. Classify the triangle in as many ways as possible. Justify your classification of the triangle according to its side lengths.

2. The degree measures of the angles of a triangle are $9x + 1$, $8x - 2$, and $9x - 1$.
   a. Find the value of x.
   b. Find the measure of each angle.
   c. Classify the triangle according to its side lengths and angle measures.

3. In isosceles triangle *ABC*, the measure of the exterior angle at base angle *B* is 135°.
   a. Find the measure of angle *B* of the triangle.
   b. Find the measure of the vertex angle.
   c. Describe the triangle.

4. In triangle *WXY*, the measures of the interior and exterior angles at vertex *Y* are $x + 15$ and $7x + 5$.
   a. Find the value of x.
   b. Find the value of the interior and exterior angles at vertex *Y*.
   c. Find the sum of the interior angles at vertices *W* and *X*.
   d. Classify the triangle in as many ways as possible.

5. The degree measure of the vertex angle of an isosceles triangle is 110°. Find the measure of a base angle. Explain how you decided.

6. The lengths of the two shorter sides of a triangle are 7 cm and 3 cm. What is the greatest possible whole number length of the longest side?

7. The lengths of two sides of a triangle are 6 and 4. What are all possible lengths of the third side?

In questions 8–10, the triangles are congruent. Explain how you would demonstrate their congruence.

8.

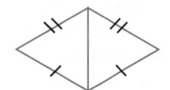

9.

10.

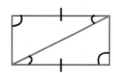

LESSON **23**
QUADRILATERALS

KEY CONCEPTS YOU'LL NEED IN THIS LESSON

1. The sum of the measures of the angles of a **quadrilateral** is 360°.

2. A **parallelogram** is a quadrilateral whose properties include:

    a. Opposite sides are parallel and congruent.

    b. A diagonal creates two congruent triangles.

    c. Opposite angles are congruent.

    d. Consecutive angles are supplementary.

    e. Diagonals bisect each other.

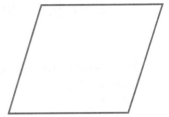

3. A **rectangle** is a parallelogram. It has all the properties of a parallelogram and:

    a. All angles are right angles.

    b. Diagonals are congruent.

4. A **rhombus** is a parallelogram. It has all the properties of a parallelogram and:

    a. All sides are congruent.

    b. Diagonals are perpendicular to each other.

    c. Diagonals bisect angles of the rhombus.

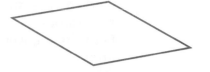

5. A **square** is a parallelogram. It has all the properties of a rectangle and a rhombus.

6. A **trapezoid** is a quadrilateral with exactly one pair of parallel sides. The parallel sides are the bases.
In an isosceles trapezoid, the non-parallel sides are congruent and the base angles are congruent.

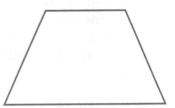

1 PARALLELOGRAMS

EXAMPLE 1

In parallelogram *ABCD*, the measure of angle A is 4x + 5 and the measure of angle C is x + 50.

a. Find the measure of angles *A* and *C*.
b. Find the measure of angle *ABC*.
c. Explain how you know that
m∠*ABD* ≅ m∠*CDB*.
d. Explain how you can demonstrate that
triangle *ABD* ≅ triangle *CDB*.

Strategy: **Use Key Concepts 1 and 2.**

Step 1: Find the measure of angles *A* and *C*. Use Key Concept 2c.
  $4x + 5 = x + 50$
  $3x + 5 = 50$
  $3x = 45$
$x = 15$, $4x + 5 = 65$, $x + 50 = 65$
So, $m\angle A = 65°$, and $m\angle C = 65°$.

Step 2: Find the measure of angle *ABC*. Use Key Concept 2d.
$65 + x = 180$
  $x = 115$
So, $m\angle ABC = 115°$.

Step 3: Explain the congruence between angle *ABD* and angle *CDB*. Use Key Concept 2a.
$\overline{AB} \parallel \overline{DC}$.
BD is a transversal that cuts $\overline{AB}$ and $\overline{DC}$.
Since angle *ABD* and angle *CDB* are alternate interior angles, they are congruent.

Step 4: Demonstrate the congruence between triangle *ABD* and triangle *CDB*. Use Key Concept 2a.
$\overline{AB} \cong \overline{CD}$, angle *ABD* ≅ angle *CDB*, $\overline{BD}$ is common to both triangles.
So, one way to demonstrate that the triangles are congruent is S.A.S. ≅ S.A.S.

EXAMPLE 2

In rectangle *RSTU*, *RT* = 3*x* + 1 and *SU* = 4*x* – 7.

a. Find the value of *x*.

b. Find the lengths of $\overline{RT}$ and $\overline{SU}$.

Strategy: **Use Key Concept 3b.**

Step 1:   Write and solve an equation based on the equality of the diagonals.

$3x + 1 = 4x - 7$

$3x + 8 = 4x$

$8 = x$

Step 2:   Find the lengths of the diagonals.

$3(8) + 1 = 25$ $4(8) - 7 = 25$

Solution: **The length of each diagonal is 25.**

EXAMPLE 3

In rhombus *WXYZ*, the length of side *WX* is 10. The measure of angle *WXY* is 120°.

Find the length of diagonal *XZ*.

Strategy: **Use Key Concept 4.**

Step 1:   Find the measure of angle *WXZ*.

Since diagonals bisect angles, $m\angle WXZ = 120 \div 2 = 60°$

Step 2:   Find the measure of angle *XWZ*.

$m\angle WXY + m\angle WZY = 120 + 120 = 240°$

So, $m\angle XWZ = (360 - 240) \div 2 = 60°$

Step 3:   Find the measure of angle *WZX*.

$60 + 60 + m\angle WZX = 180$, so

$m\angle WZX = 60°$ and triangle *XWZ* is an equiangular and equilateral triangle.

Solution: **The length of diagonal *XZ* = 10.**

EXAMPLE 4	**Describe the triangle formed by one diagonal of the square and two sides.**	

Strategy: **Use Key Concept 5.**

Step 1: Describe the sides.
Since in a square all sides are equal, $\overline{MN} \cong \overline{NP}$.

Step 2: Describe the angles.
Since in a square all angles are right angles, $m\angle MNP = 90°$.
Also, since diagonals bisect angles, $m\angle NMP = 45°$ and $m\angle NPM = 45°$

Solution: **Triangle *MNP* is an isosceles right triangle. (By the same reasoning, triangle *MQP* is also an isosceles right triangle.)**

EXAMPLE 5 **In isosceles trapezoid *ABCD* with diagonal $\overline{BD}$, the angles are as shown. Find the measure of angle *C*.**

Strategy: **Use Key Concept 6.**

Step 1: Find the measure of angle *CBD*.
$\overline{BD}$ is a transversal that cuts parallel lines *AD* and *BC*.
So, $m\angle CBD = 20°$.

Step 2: Find the measure of angle *C*.
$m\angle C = 180 - (50 + 20) = 110°$.

Solution: **The measure of angle *C* is 110°.**

REGENTS MATH PRACTICE

1. The degree measures of two opposite angles of a parallelogram are $7x + 10$ and $10x - 20$.
   a. Find the value of x.
   b. Find the degree measures of each angle of the parallelogram.
   c. What properties of a parallelogram allow you to find the measures of all four angles?

2. Two consecutive angles of a rhombus have the following degree measures: $2x + 5$ and $5x$.
   a. Find the value of x.
   b. Find the measures of each angle.
   c. Name the property of a rhombus that allows you to find the measures of each angle.

3. In rhombus $ABCD$, the measure of angle A is $2x + 10$. The measure of angle C is $3x - 30$. Describe the rhombus and justify your explanation.

4. In rhombus $QRST$, the measure of angle Q is $60°$ and the length of diagonal RT is 12. Find the length of a side of the rhombus. Explain your reasoning.

5. In rectangle $ABCD$, the length of diagonal AC is $5x - 10$. The length of diagonal BD is $3x + 2$.
   a. Find the value of x.
   b. Find the length of each diagonal.
   c. If side AD is $2x + 4$, find the length of side AB.

6. In isosceles trapezoid $STUV$, $m\angle S = 70°$, $m\angle VTU = 30°$. Find the measure of $\angle SVT$ and $\angle TUV$.

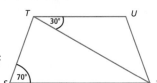

In questions 7–10, decide whether the statement is always true. If it is, write true. If it is not always true, write false.

7. A quadrilateral with two consecutive supplementary angles is a parallelogram.

8. Every rhombus is a square.

9. If the diagonals of a quadrilateral bisect one another, the quadrilateral is a square.

10. A quadrilateral must have at least one acute angle.

UNIT ④ REVIEW

1. Two angles of a triangle are complementary and in the ratio of 2:1. Find the measure of each angle of the triangle. Describe the triangle according to its sides and angles.

2. What is an expression for an angle that is supplementary to an angle that measures $x°$?

Use the diagram to answer questions 3 and 4. $\overleftrightarrow{AB}$ and $\overleftrightarrow{CD}$ are parallel and $\overleftrightarrow{EF}$ is a transversal.

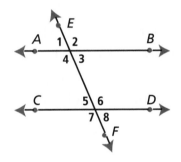

3. What is the sum of the measures of angles 3 and 4? Give one explanation of your answer.

4. What is the sum of the measures of angles 3 and 6? Give one explanation of your answer.

5. For which polygon will the sum of the interior and exterior angles be equal?

6. Find the number of sides in a polygon if the sum of the interior angles is 1,440°. If the polygon is regular, what is the measure of each interior angle? each exterior angle?

7. In isosceles triangle ABC, the measures of base angles A and B are each 15° greater than the measure of vertex angle C. Find the measure of each angle of the triangle.

8. The lengths of two sides of a triangle are 7 and 11. Find all possible lengths of the third side.

9. The degree measures of two consecutive angles of a parallelogram are $4x - 10$ and $3x + 15$. Find the value of x. Describe the parallelogram.

10. Can the parallelogram described in question 9 above be a square? Justify your answer.

Notice: Photocopying any part of this book is forbidden by law.

97

LESSON ㉔
PERIMETER AND AREA

KEY CONCEPTS YOU'LL NEED IN THIS LESSON

1. The **perimeter** of a polygon is the sum of the lengths of its sides. Perimeter is measured in units.

    Perimeter formulas are:

    Triangle: $P = a + b + c$, where a, b, and c are side lengths.

    Square: $P = 4s$, where s is the length of a side.

    Rectangle: $P = 2l + 2w$ or $2b + 2h$, where l or b is the length and w or h is the width.

2. The **area** of a figure is the number of square units it can contain.

    Area formulas are:

    Rectangle: $A = bh$, where b is the length of the base and h the height.

    Parallelogram: $A = bh$, where b and h are the base and height respectively. The height is perpendicular to the base.

    Square: $A = s^2$, where s is the length of a side.

    Trapezoid: $A = \frac{h(b_1 + b_2)}{2}$, where h is the height, and b_1 and b_2 are the bases.

    Triangle: $A = \frac{bh}{2}$, where b is the length of the base and h is the height. The height is always perpendicular to the base.

    Rhombus: $A = \frac{1}{2}(d_1)(d_2)$, where d_1 and d_2 are the lengths of the diagonals.

---

① PERIMETER

EXAMPLE 1

A standard ping-pong table has a length that is 1 ft less than twice its width. Its perimeter is 28 ft. What are its length and width?

Strategy: Use Key Concept 1.

Step 1: Define the length and width using a variable.
Let x = the width of the table.
Let $2x - 1$ = the length of the table.

Step 2: Set up and solve an equation from the data in the problem.
$$2(2x - 1) + 2x = 28$$
$$4x - 2 + 2x = 28$$
$$6x - 2 = 28$$

$6x = 30$

$x = 5;$ $2x - 1 = 9$

Solution: **The width of the table is 5 ft, and the length is 9 ft.**

EXAMPLE 2

The length of a rectangle is twice the side of a square. The width of the rectangle is 7 less than the side of the square. If the perimeter of the rectangle is 10 more than the perimeter of the square, find the length of a side of the square and the dimensions of the rectangle.

x $2x$ $x - 7$

Strategy: **Use Key Concept 1.**

Step 1: Define the side lengths using a variable.
Let x = the side of the square.
Let $2x$ = the length of the rectangle.
Let $x - 7$ = the width of the rectangle.

Step 2: Set up and solve an equation using the data from the problem.
$$2(2x) + 2(x - 7) = 4x + 10$$
$$4x + 2x - 14 = 4x + 10$$
$$6x - 14 = 4x + 10$$
$$6x = 4x + 24$$
$$2x = 24$$
$$x = 12$$

Solution: **The length of a side of the square is 12 units. The length of the rectangle is 24 units and the width of the rectangle is 5 units.**

EXAMPLE 3

If the length of a side of a square is doubled, what is the effect on the perimeter of the square?

Strategy: **Same as Example 1.**

Step 1: Write the perimeter formula for a square.
$P = 4s$

Step 2: Double the length of the side.

$P_2 = 4(2s) = 8s$

Step 3: Write a ratio to compare the perimeters.

$\dfrac{P_2}{P} = \dfrac{8s}{4s} = \dfrac{8}{4} = \dfrac{2}{1}$

Solution: **If the length of a side of a square is doubled, the perimeter is doubled.**

2 AREA

EXAMPLE 4 The ratio of two consecutive sides of a rectangle is 5:6. If the area of the rectangle is 120 m², find its dimensions.

Strategy: **Use Key Concept 2.**

Step1: Define the length and width using a variable.
Let $5x$ = the shorter side.
Let $6x$ = the longer side.

Step 2: Write and solve an equation.
$5x(6x) = 120$
$30x^2 = 120$
$x^2 = 4$
$x = \sqrt{4} = 2$

Solution: **The shorter side of the rectangle is $5x = 5(2) = 10$ m.**
The longer side of the rectangle is $6x = 6(2) = 12$ m.

EXAMPLE 5 If the length of each side of a rectangle is doubled, what is the effect on the area?

Strategy: **Same as Example 4.**

Step 1: Write the formula for the area of a rectangle.
$A = bh$

Step 2: Write the formula, doubling each dimension.
$A_2 = (2b)(2h) = 4bh$

Step 3: Write a ratio to compare the areas.
$\dfrac{A_2}{A} = \dfrac{4bh}{bh} = \dfrac{4}{1}$

Solution: **If the length of each side of a rectangle is doubled, the area is multiplied by 4.**

REGENTS MATH PRACTICE

1. The length of a side of regular pentagon QRSTU is represented by $4x - 3$. What is an expression for the perimeter of the figure?

2. Each side of a regular hexagon is represented by $2x + 1$. The perimeter of the hexagon is 114 ft. Find the value of x.

3. The perimeter of a square is 64 in. What is the area of the square?

4. In an isosceles triangle, the length of the base is 5 cm shorter than each of the other sides. The perimeter of the triangle is 76 cm. Find the length of each side.

5. In the parallelogram at the right, the length of the base is 45 m, the altitude is 24 m, and the dashed extension of the base is 10 m. Find the perimeter of the parallelogram. (*Hint: Consider how you can apply the Pythagorean Theorem.*)

6. A square has side 10. If the length of each side is multiplied by 3, what is the new perimeter?

7. The base of a triangle is $3x$ and the altitude to that base is $3x + 1$. If the area of the triangle is 45 ft², find the length of the base.

8. The base of a parallelogram is $5x$ and its altitude is $3x + 1$. The area of the figure is 70 cm². Find the length of the base and altitude.

9. The area of a trapezoid is 102 ft². The height is 6 ft and the bases are represented by $2x$ and $2x + 6$. Find the value of x.

10. In a rhombus, the length of the shorter diagonal is $2x$ and the length of the longer diagonal is $3x$. If the area of the rhombus is 12, find the value of x.

11. The sum of the areas of two squares is 170 in.² If the length of a side of one square is 4 more than the length of a side of the other square, find the length of a side of each square.

12. A triangle has an area of 12 m². If the base of the triangle is doubled, but the altitude to the base is unchanged, what is the new area?

13. A rectangle has length 10 and width 4. If each dimension is halved, what is the effect on the area?

LESSON 25
THE COORDINATE PLANE

KEY CONCEPTS YOU'LL NEED IN THIS LESSON

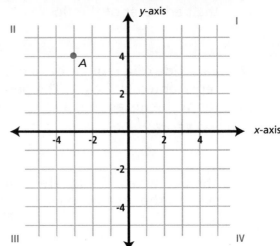

1. The horizontal axis (the *x*-axis) and the vertical axis (the *y*-axis) meet at the point (0, 0), the **origin**.

2. The axes divide the plane into **4 quadrants** as shown.

3. A point can be named by identifying its *x*-coordinate (its **abscissa**) and its *y*-coordinate (its **ordinate**). The location (-3, 4) describes the **coordinates** of point A.

4. Lengths of line segments parallel to either axis can be found by using absolute values. For a horizontal line: Find the absolute value of difference of the *x*-coordinates or abscissas.
   For a vertical line: Find the absolute value of the difference of the *y*-coordinates or ordinates.
   The length of a line segment not parallel to either axis can be found by using the **distance formula**: $d = \sqrt{(x_2 - x_1)^2 + (y_2 - y_1)^2}$

5. The coordinates of the midpoint of a horizontal or vertical line segment can be found by counting units. The coordinates of the midpoint of a segment not parallel to either axis can be found by using the **midpoint formula**:

   $x_m = \dfrac{x_1 + x_2}{2}$ and $y_m = \dfrac{y_1 + y_2}{2}$ where (x_1, y_1) and (x_2, y_2) are the coordinates of the endpoints, and (x_m, y_m) are the coordinates of the midpoint.

6. Perimeters and areas of figures on the coordinate plane can be found by using formulas.

1 DISTANCE ON THE COORDINATE PLANE

EXAMPLE 1

Find the length of the line segment at the right.

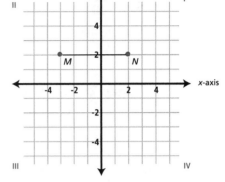

Strategy: **Use Key Concepts 1 – 4.**

Step 1: Line segment *MN* is horizontal. Therefore, find the absolute value of the difference of the *x*-coordinates (or abscissas) of the endpoints.

The coordinates of *M* are (-3, 2). The coordinates of *N* are (2, 2). The absolute value of the difference of the *x*-coordinates = $|-3 - 2| = |-5| = 5$ or $|2 - (-3)| = |5| = 5$

Solution: **The length of a line segment with endpoints (-3, 2) and (2, 2) is 5.**

EXAMPLE 2

Find the length of a line segment with endpoints (4, 5) and (4, -2).

Strategy: **Use Key Concepts 1 – 4.**

Step 1: The line is vertical. You need to find the absolute value of the difference between the *y*-coordinates or ordinates.

$$|5 - (-2)| = |7| = 7 \text{ or } |(-2) - 5| = |-7| = 7$$

Solution: **The length of a line segment with endpoints (4, 5) and (4, -2) is 7.**

EXAMPLE 3

Find the length of the line segment with endpoints $A(7, 6)$ and $B(-5, 1)$.

Strategy: **Use Key Concept 4, the distance formula.**

Step 1: Let (7, 6) be (x_1, y_1), making $x_1 = 7$ and $y_1 = 6$.
Let (-5, 1) be (x_2, y_2), making $x_2 = -5$ and $y_2 = 1$.

Step 2: Use the distance formula: $d = \sqrt{(x_2 - x_1)^2 + (y_2 - y_1)^2}$
$d = \sqrt{(-5 - 7)^2 + (1 - 6)^2}$
$d = \sqrt{(-12)^2 + (-5)^2}$
$d = \sqrt{144 + 25} = \sqrt{169} = 13$

Solution: **The length of a line segment with endpoints (7, 6) and (-5, 1) is 13 units.**

EXAMPLE 4

In a circle with center at point *0*, the endpoints of a diameter are (5, 9) and (2, 0). Find the coordinates of the center of the circle.

Strategy: Use Key Concept 5.

Step 1: Let (5, 9) be (x_1, y_1), making $x_1 = 5$ and $y_1 = 9$.
Let (2, 0) be (x_2, y_2), making $x_2 = 2$ and $y_2 = 0$.

Step 2: Use the midpoint formula to find the midpoint of the segment connecting the points.

$$x_m = \frac{x_1 + x_2}{2} = \frac{5 + 2}{2} = \frac{7}{2} = 3.5 \qquad y_m = \frac{y_1 + y_2}{2} = \frac{9 + 0}{2} = \frac{9}{2} = 4.5$$

The midpoint of the segment is at (3.5, 4.5).

Solution: A circle having a diameter with the given endpoints has its center at (3.5, 4.5).

2 PERIMETER AND AREA

EXAMPLE 5

Find the perimeter and area of a rectangle with vertices at the following coordinates: *Q*(0, 0), *R*(-6, 0), *S*(-6, -3), and *T*(0, -3).

Strategy: Use Key Concepts 4, 5, and 6.

Step 1: Find the length of the rectangle. Use side *QR* as the length.
Find the absolute value of the difference in the *x*-coordinates.
$|0 - (-6)| = |6| = 6$

Step 2: Find the width of the rectangle. Use side *RS* as the width.
Find the absolute value of the difference in the *y*-coordinates.
$|0 - (-3)| = |3| = 3$

Step 3: Use the perimeter formula for a rectangle.
$P = 2l + 2w = 2(6) + 2(3) = 12 + 6 = 18$

Step 4: Find the area. Use the area formula for a rectangle.
$A = lw = 6(3) = 18$

Solution: A rectangle with the given vertices has a perimeter of 18 units and area of 18 units².

EXAMPLE 6 — Find the area of a trapezoid with the following vertices: $A(2, 0)$, $B(8, 0)$, $C(7, 3)$, and $D(3, 3)$.

Strategy: Use Key Concepts 4 and 6.

Step 1: Find the length of each base and the height.
b_1: $|8 - 2| = |6| = 6$
b_2: $|7 - 3| = |4| = 4$
h : $|3 - 0| = |3| = 3$

Step 2: Use the area formula for a trapezoid.
$A = \frac{h(b_1 + b_2)}{2} = \frac{3(6 + 4)}{2} = \frac{3(10)}{2} = 15$ units^2

Solution: **The area of the trapezoid is 15 units^2.**

EXAMPLE 7 — Find the area of a rhombus whose vertices are $A(3, 1)$, $B(1, 6)$, $C(-1, 1)$ and $D(1, -4)$.

Strategy: Use Key Concepts 4 and 6.

Step 1: Find the lengths of the diagonals.
$d_1 = AC = |3 - (-1)| = |3 + 1| = |4| = 4$
$d_2 = BD = |6 - (-4)| = |6 + 4| = |10| = 10$

Step 2: Find the area. Use the formula $A = \frac{1}{2}(d_1)(d_2)$
$A = \frac{1}{2}(4)(10) = \frac{1}{2}(40) = 20$

Solution: **The area of the rhombus with the given vertices is 20 units^2.**

REGENTS MATH PRACTICE

In questions 1–5, find the length of line segments with the following endpoints. If necessary, leave answers in radical form.

1. (0, -4) and (0, 5)

2. (7, -2) and (13, -2)

3. (-5, -1) and (-5, 8)

4. (4, 5) and (-2, 1)

5. (-3, 5) and (5, -3)

6. Explain how you can tell by examining the endpoints whether a line segment is horizontal or vertical.

In problems 7–10, first identify the type of polygon that would be formed by connecting the vertices in order. Then find the perimeter of the figure.

7. $A(2, 1)$, $B(7, 1)$, $C(7, 6)$, $D(2, 6)$

8. $W(-2, 3)$, $X(-2, 5)$, $Y(4, 5)$, $Z(4, 3)$

9. $P(0, 0)$, $Q(0, 10)$, $R(6, 10)$, $S(6, 0)$

10. $B(0, 0)$, $C(4, 0)$, $D(4, 3)$

In problems 11–14, identify the figure. Then find its area.

11. $D(0, 0)$, $E(1, 5)$, $F(4, 5)$, $G(5, 0)$

12. $P(-6, 0)$, $Q(-6, 6)$, $R(-3, 3)$

13. $B(1, 0)$, $C(3, 7)$, $D(9, 7)$, $E(7, 0)$

14. $R(-5, 0)$, $S(0, 4)$, $T(5, 0)$, $U(0, -4)$

LESSON (26)
THE CIRCLE

KEY CONCEPTS YOU'LL NEED IN THIS LESSON

1. The ratio of the **circumference** of a circle to its diameter is π, approximately 3.14.

2. The formula for the circumference of a circle is $C = \pi d$ where d is the diameter of the circle or $C = 2\pi r$ where r is the radius of the circle.

3. The formula for the **area** of a circle is $A = \pi r^2$ where r is the radius of the circle.

---

1 CIRCUMFERENCE

EXAMPLE 1

A circle has a radius of 12 in. Find its circumference:
a. in terms of π and
b. to the nearest tenth of an inch.

Strategy: **Use Key Concepts 1 and 2.**

Step 1: Find the circumference in terms of π.
$C = 2\pi r = 2(12)\,\pi = 24\pi$ in.

Step 2: Find the circumference to the nearest tenth of an inch.
$C = 2\pi r = 2(3.14)(12) \approx 75.4$ in.

Solution: **For a circle with radius 12 in., the circumference is 24π in. or approximately 75.4 in.**

EXAMPLE 2

What is the radius of a circle if its circumference is 16?

Strategy: **Same as above.**

Step 1: Use the formula for circumference: $C = 2\pi r$.
Solve the formula for r.

$C = 2\pi r$
$\dfrac{C}{2\pi} = r$

Notice: Photocopying any part of this book is forbidden by law.

Step 2: Substitute the value 16 for C.

$$r = \frac{16}{2\pi} = \frac{8}{\pi}$$

Solution: A circle with circumference 16 has a radius of $\frac{8}{\pi}$ units.

EXAMPLE 3 If the radius of a circle is doubled, what is the effect on the circumference.

Strategy: Use Key Concepts 1 and 2.

Step 1: Write the formula for the circumference of a circle using the radius:
$C = 2\pi r$

Step 2: Multiply the length of the radius by 2.
$C_2 = 2(2)\,\pi r$

Step 3: Write a ratio to compare the two measures.
$$\frac{C_2}{C} = \frac{2(2)\,\pi r}{2\pi r} = \frac{4\pi r}{2\pi r} = \frac{4}{2} = \frac{2}{1}$$

Solution: Doubling the radius of a circle doubles the circumference.

2 AREA

EXAMPLE 4 A circle has a diameter of 8 cm. Find its area
a. in terms of π and
b. to the nearest square cm.

Strategy: Use Key Concept 3.

Step 1: Find the radius of the circle.
$r = \frac{d}{2} = \frac{8}{2} = 4$ cm

Step 2: Find the area in terms of π.
$A = \pi r^2$
$A = \pi(4)^2 = 16\pi$ cm²

Step 3: Find the area to the nearest square cm.
$A = \pi r^2$
$A \approx 3.14(4)^2 \approx 3.14(16) \approx 50.24 \approx 50$ cm²

Solution: For a circle with radius 8 cm, the area is 16π cm² or approximately 50 cm².

EXAMPLE 5

A circle has area 25π. Find its diameter.

Strategy: Same as Example 4

Step 1: Find the radius.

$$A = \pi r^2$$
$$25\pi = \pi r^2$$
$$25 = r^2$$
$$\sqrt{25} = r$$
$$r = 5$$

Step 2: Find the diameter.
$$d = 2r = 2(5) = 10$$

Solution: **For a circle with area 25π, the diameter is 10 units.**

EXAMPLE 6

If the radius of a circle is doubled, what is the effect on the area?

Strategy: **Same as Example 4.**

Step 1: Write the formula for the area of a circle.
$$A = \pi r^2$$

Step 2: Multiply the length of the radius by 2.
$$A_2 = \pi (2r)^2$$

Step 3: Write a ratio to compare the areas.
$$\frac{A_2}{A} = \frac{\pi (2r)^2}{\pi r^2} = \frac{\pi (2r)(2r)}{\pi r^2} = \frac{\pi (4r)^2}{\pi r^2} = \frac{4}{1}$$

Solution: **If the radius of a circle is doubled, the area is multiplied by 4.**

REGENTS MATH PRACTICE

1. To the nearest inch, how far does a bicycle wheel with radius 13 in. travel in one turn?

2. A circular arena is 120 m across it widest part. What is the circumference of the arena to the nearest meter?

3. The circumference of a circle is 24. What is its diameter?

4. If a circle has circumference 36, what is its radius?

5. If the radius of a circle is multiplied by 4, what is the effect on the circumference? Explain your answer.

6. A circle has a diameter of 18 cm. Find its area expressed in terms of π.

7. Find the radius of a circle whose area is 64π.

8. Find the circumference of a circle in terms of π whose area is 49π.

9. If the diameter of a circle is multiplied by 4, what is the effect on the area? Explain your answer.

10. If the radius of a circle is halved, what is the effect on the area?

LESSON 27
SOLVING AREA PROBLEMS

KEY CONCEPTS YOU'LL NEED IN THIS LESSON

1. A figure may be **inscribed** in another figure or **circumscribed** about another figure.

 The square is inscribed in the circle. All the vertices of the square are on the circle. Each diagonal of the square is also a diameter of the circle. The circle is circumscribed about the square.

 The circle is inscribed in the square. The diameter of the circle is equal to the side of the square. The square is circumscribed about the circle.

2. The area formula for a semicircle is $A = \frac{\pi r^2}{2}$.

---

1 FINDING A PARTIAL AREA

EXAMPLE 1

Figure *ABCD* is a trapezoid. Figure *BCDE* is a square. The diameter of the circle is 12.
a. Find the length of $\overline{BE}$.
b. Find the length of $\overline{AD}$.
c. Find the area of the circle in terms of π.
d. Find the area of the shaded region in terms of π and to the nearest whole number. Use 3.14 as π.

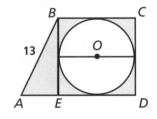

Strategy: Use Key Concept 1.

Step 1: Find the length of $\overline{BE}$.
Since circle *O* is inscribed in the square, the diameter of the circle is equal to a side of the square. *BE* = 12

Step 2: Find the length of $\overline{AD}$.
Find *AE* using the Pythagorean Theorem. Since *BCDE* is a square, $m\angle BED$ and $m\angle AEB = 90°$. Triangle *ABE* is a right triangle and $a^2 + b^2 = c^2$ or $AB^2 = AE^2 + BE^2$

Notice: Photocopying any part of this book is forbidden by law.

$$13^2 = AE^2 + 12^2$$
$$169 = AE^2 + 144$$
$$25 = AE^2$$

So, $AE = \sqrt{25} = 5$
$AD = AE + ED = 5 + 12 = 17$

Step 3:   Find the area of circle O in terms of π.
$A = \pi r^2 = \pi(6)^2 = 36\pi$

Step 4:   Find the area of the shaded region.

Area of shaded region = Total area – area of circle =

(Area of square + area of triangle) – area of circle

$= 144 + \frac{5(12)}{2} - 36\pi$

$= 144 + 30 - 36\pi = 174 - 36\pi$

$\approx 174 - 36(3.14) \approx 61$ units²

Solution: **$BE = 12$, $AD = 17$, area of circle = 36π, and area of shaded region ≈ 61 units²**

---

2   FINDING A COMPOUND AREA

EXAMPLE 2   **$QRST$ is a rectangle. $QR = 16$, $QT = 8$**
$\overset{\frown}{QR}$, $\overset{\frown}{ST}$, $\overset{\frown}{RS}$, and $\overset{\frown}{QT}$ are semicircles.

Find the area of the figure in terms of π and to the nearest whole number.

Strategy: **Use Key Concepts 1 and 2.**

Step 1:   Make a plan to ensure that you include all the parts.
Area = Area of rectangle + 2(area of larger semicircle) +
2(area of smaller semicircle)

Step 2:   Find the area of the rectangle.
Area = lw = 16(8) = 128

Step 3:   Find the area of each pair of semicircles.
Area of larger pair of semicircles = $2(\frac{\pi r^2}{2}) = \pi r^2 = \pi(8)^2 = 64\pi$
Area of smaller pair of semicircles = $2(\frac{\pi r^2}{2}) = \pi r^2 = \pi(4)^2 = 16\pi$

Step 4:   Add the parts.
$128 + 64\pi + 16\pi = (128 + 80\pi)$ units²
$128 + 80(3.14) \approx 379$ units²

Solution: **The area of the figure = (128 + 80π) units² $\approx$ 379 units².**

REGENTS MATH PRACTICE

In problems 1–5, find the area of the shaded region to the nearest whole number. Use 3.14 for π. For each problem, describe the steps you took.

1.   Diameter of circle = 24 cm

2.   Diameter of circle = 14 in.

3.   Diameter of larger circle = 12 ft
     Diameter of smaller circle = 7 ft

4.   Diameter of circle = 16 cm
     Triangle ABC is a right triangle.
     AB = 5, BC = 13

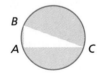

5.   ABCD is a rectangle inscribed in the circle.
     AB = 9, AC = 12
     ABD is a right triangle in which $\overline{BC}$ is a diameter of the circle.

In problems 6–10, find the area of the entire figure to the nearest whole number. Use 3.14 for π.

6.   Semicircle $\widehat{AE}$ is connected to rectangle ABDE.
     Triangle BCD is a right triangle.
     BD = 24, AB = 30, CE = 37

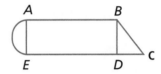

7.   QRST is an isosceles trapezoid.
     $\widehat{RS}$ is a semicircle.
     RS = 14, QT = 22
     RU, the height of the trapezoid, = 12

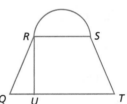

8.   LMNP is a parallelogram.
     MN = 12, MQ = 8, ML = 10

9.   AB = BC = CD = 14, m∠B = m∠C = 90°
     $\widehat{AD}$ is a semicircle.

10. FG = HJ = 20
     $\widehat{FJ}$ and $\widehat{GH}$ are semicircles.

LESSON 28
VOLUME

KEY CONCEPTS YOU'LL NEED IN THIS LESSON

1. Volume is measured in **cubic units**, the number of unit cubes a solid can contain.

2. **Right prisms** are solids with 2 congruent bases and with height perpendicular to the bases. The volume V of a right prism is V = area of base × height or $V = bh$

Right prisms include:

cube

rectangular solid

triangular prism

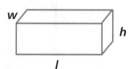

Volume = e^3

Volume = $l \times w \times h$

Volume = $B \times h$

Other **right solids** include:

pyramid

cylinder

cone

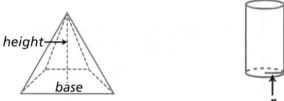

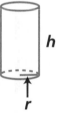

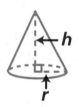

Volume = $\frac{1}{3}$ Area of base × h

Volume = $\pi r^2 h$

Volume = $\frac{1}{3} \pi r^2 h$

3. The volume of a sphere with radius $r = \frac{4}{3}\pi r^3$

4. Some problems require conversion between units of volume.
   1 liter = 1,000 cm³

1 SOLVING VOLUME PROBLEMS

EXAMPLE 1

The volume of a rectangular solid is 135 cm³. Find the height of the solid if the length of the base is 6 cm and the width is 3 cm.

Strategy: **Use Key Concepts 1 and 2.**

Step 1: Write the appropriate formula.
$V = lwh$.

Step 2: Substitute known values into the formula and solve for the missing value.
$$135 = 6 \times 3 \times h$$
$$135 = 18h$$
$$7.5 = h$$

Solution: **The height of the rectangular solid is 7.5 cm.**

EXAMPLE 2

The edge of a cube is represented by 3x. Find the volume of the cube.

Strategy: **Use Key Concepts 1 and 2.**

Step 1: Write the formula for the volume of a cube.
$V = e^3$

Step 2: Substitute the value for the edge in the formula.
$V = (3x)^3 = 3x(3x)(3x) = 27x^3$

Solution: **A cube with edge 3x has volume 27x³.**

EXAMPLE 3

The volume of a rectangular solid is 72 in.³ The length of the base is 1 more than twice the width. The height is 2 in. Find the dimensions of the solid.

Strategy: **Use Key Concept 2.**

Step 1: Follow algebraic problem solving technique. Define the variables from the data in the problem.
Let x = the width of the base
Let $2x + 1$ = the length of the base

Step 2: Write and solve an equation that describes the relationships in the problem. Use the formula for the volume of a rectangular solid:

$V = lwh$

$$(2x + 1)(x)2 = 72$$
$$(2x + 1)2x = 72$$
$$4x^2 + 2x = 72$$
$$4x^2 + 2x - 72 = 0$$
$$2x^2 + x - 36 = 0$$
$$(2x + 9)(x - 4) = 0$$

$$
\begin{array}{c|c}
2x + 9 = 0 & x - 4 = 0 \\
2x = -9 & x = 4 \\
x = -4.5 & \\
\text{Reject} &
\end{array}
$$

Step 3: Write the solution to the problem.
The width of the base = 4 in., the length of the base = 9 in.

Step 4: Check the problem.
$V = lwh$
$72 = 2 \times 4 \times 9$?
$72 = 72$ ✔

---

② CHANGING DIMENSIONS

EXAMPLE 4 — **The radius of a cylinder is 3 ft. Its height is 5 ft. What is the effect on the volume if the radius is doubled?**

Strategy: **Use Key Concept 2.**

Step 1: Write the volume formula for a cylinder.
$V = \pi r^2 h$

Step 2: Substitute the known values into the formula.
$V = \pi(3)^2(5) = \pi(9)(5)$
$V = 45\pi$

Step 3: Double the radius to find the new volume.
$V_2 = \pi(6)^2 5 = \pi(36)(5)$
$V_2 = 180\pi$

Step 4: Divide to find the factor by which the volume has changed.
$\dfrac{V_2}{V} = \dfrac{180\pi}{45\pi} = 4$

Solution: **By doubling the radius of a cylinder, the volume becomes 4 times greater.**

EXAMPLE 5　　What is the effect on the volume of a sphere if its radius is doubled?

Strategy:　　**Use Key Concept 4.**

Step 1:　　Write the volume formula for a sphere.
$V = \frac{4}{3}\pi r^3$

Step 2:　　Double the radius and simplify the result.
$V_2 = \frac{4}{3}\pi(2r)^3 = \frac{4}{3}\pi(2r)(2r)(2r) = \frac{4}{3}\pi(8r^3)$

Step 3:　　Divide to find the effect on the volume.
$\dfrac{V_2}{V} = \dfrac{\frac{4}{3}\pi(8r^3)}{\frac{4}{3}\pi r^3} = 8$

Solution:　　**By doubling the radius of a sphere, the volume is increased 8 times.**

3 CONVERTING BETWEEN UNITS

EXAMPLE 6　　**A small fish tank in the shape of a rectangular prism measures 40 cm by 50 cm by 30 cm. It takes 30 seconds to put a liter of water into the tank. How long will it take to fill the tank at that rate?**

Strategy:　　**Use Key Concepts 2 and 4.**

Step 1:　　Find the volume of the tank in cm³.
Volume = lwh = 40 × 50 × 30 = 60,000 cm³

Step 2:　　Find the number of liters that are equivalent to 60,000 cm³.
60,000 ÷ 1,000 = 60 liters

Step 3:　　Find the number of minutes needed to fill the tank.
30 seconds = 0.5 minutes, so
60 (0.50) = 30 minutes　　or　　60 ÷ 2 = 30 minutes

Solution:　　**It will take 30 minutes to fill the tank at the rate of 1 liter per 30 seconds.**

REGENTS MATH PRACTICE

1. The edge of a cube measures 4 in. What is the volume of the cube?

2. The volume of a cube is 27 cm³. What is the area of one face of the cube? Explain your reasoning.

3. The base of a triangular prism measures 24 in.² and the volume is 168 in.³ What is the height of the prism?

4. A square pyramid has a volume of 32 ft³. The length of one side of the base is 4 ft. What is the height of the pyramid?

5. In a rectangular prism, the length of the base is 8 cm. The width of the base is 1 cm less than twice the height. If the volume is 120 cm³, find the height of the figure. Describe the procedure you used.

6. Find the volume of a cone in terms of π whose radius measures 5 in. and whose height is 3 in.

7. What is the effect of doubling the edge of a cube on the cube's volume?

8. A plant is removed from a pot in the shape of a cube with an edge of 3 in. It is replanted in a pot in the shape of a cube with an edge of 9 in. How many times greater is the volume of the larger pot than the original?

9. How many times greater is the volume of a cylinder than a cone with the same radius and height?

   How do the formulas for the two figures help you answer the question?

10. A triangular prism has a base that is in the shape of a right triangle. The legs of the triangle measure 6 cm and 8 cm. If the length of each leg is doubled and the height remains unchanged, what is the effect on the volume of the prism?

11. A storage tank in the shape of a rectangular prism measures 150 cm by 100 cm by 90 cm. What is the maximum number of 1 liter containers of liquid that can be filled from the tank?

12. A tank in the shape of a cube has an edge 40 cm long. How long would it take to fill the tank if a liter container is used and 1 liter can be added every 15 seconds? Show the work you did to arrive at your answer.

UNIT 5 REVIEW

1. The length of each side of a square frame is increased by 5 inches. The area of the new frame is 289 in.^{2} Explain how you would find the length of each side of the original frame.

2. A trapezoid with height 10, has bases represented by $3x$ and $3x + 6$. If the area of the trapezoid is 270, find the length of each base.

3. Explain how you would use the Pythagorean Theorem to find the length of a line segment with endpoints at (-3, 5) and (4, 7). Then find the length of the segment.

4. Explain how you know that the polygon with vertices at (0, 0), (0, 5), (7, 5), and (7, 0) is a rectangle. Then find its area.

5. Two circles share the same center. One has a radius of 9 cm. The other has a radius of 18 cm. How many times greater is the area of the larger circle than the smaller?

6. The circumference of a circle is 60. Find the radius of the circle in terms of π.

7. The area of a circle is 100π. Find its circumference in terms of π.

8. The area used for a soccer field is a rectangle 110 yd long by 80 yd wide. If a semicircular seating area with a diameter equal to the width of the field is located at each end, what is the total area of the field and the two seating areas? Use 3.14 for π.

9. A wood display cube has a volume of 8 ft^3. If identical cubes are used, what is the volume of the next largest cube that can be built using display cubes? Explain your reasoning.

10. By how many times must the radius of a sphere be increased in order to increase the volume 27 times?

Notice: Photocopying any part of this book is forbidden by law.

119

LESSON 29
RATIO, PROPORTION, AND PERCENT

KEY CONCEPTS YOU'LL NEED IN THIS LESSON

1. A **ratio** is a comparison of two numbers using division. A ratio is usually expressed in one of the following ways:

    $x : y$ or $\dfrac{x}{y}$ $4:9$ or $\dfrac{4}{9}$

    A ratio may involve more than two numbers: $2:5:7$

2. A ratio is used to compare numbers that are measured in the same unit. When numbers in a ratio are in different units, the ratio is a **rate**.

    $\dfrac{195 \text{ mi}}{3h} = \dfrac{65 \text{ mi}}{h}$ $\leftarrow$ The rate is in lowest terms and is expressed using units.

3. A **proportion** is an equation showing that two ratios are equivalent. A proportion has 4 terms.

    $\dfrac{\text{extreme}}{\text{mean}} = \dfrac{\text{mean}}{\text{extreme}}$

    In a proportion, the product of the means equals the product of the extremes (cross products are equal).

4. If you know three terms, you can find the missing term (**solve the proportion**) by using cross products.

    $\dfrac{x}{7} = \dfrac{15}{35}$

    $35x = 7.15$ Use cross products.
    $35x = 105$
    $x = 3$

5. Percent is a ratio that compares a number to 100. A percent can be written as a fraction or a decimal.

    $18\% = \dfrac{18}{100} = 0.18$

    $120\% = \dfrac{120}{100} = 1.2$

    $0.7\% = \dfrac{0.7}{100} = \dfrac{7}{1{,}000} = 0.007$

    $12\frac{1}{2}\% = \dfrac{12\frac{1}{2}}{100} = \dfrac{125}{1{,}000} = 0.125$

    Many problems about discounts, markups, sales commissions, and taxes involve percents.

1 RATIO

EXAMPLE 1

In an isosceles triangle, the base is 6 and the perimeter is 22. Find the ratio of the base to a leg.

Strategy: **Use Key Concept 1.**

Step 1: Find the length of a leg of the triangle. Recall that in an isosceles triangle, the two legs are congruent.
Let x = the length of a leg
$$2x + 6 = 22$$
$$2x = 16$$
$$x = 8, \text{ the length of each leg}$$

Step 2: Write the ratio of the base to a leg.
$$\frac{\text{Base}}{\text{Leg}} = \frac{6}{8}$$

Solution: **In lowest terms, the ratio of the base to a leg is $\frac{3}{4}$ or 3:4.**

EXAMPLE 2

The ninth grade at Cleveland High School has 243 students in 9 classes. The ninth grade at Garfield High has 286 students in 11 classes. Which school has more students per class?

Strategy: **Use Key Concept 2.**

Step 1: Write a ratio for each school. Simplify each ratio.
Cleveland   Garfield
$$\frac{243}{9} = \frac{27}{1} \qquad \frac{286}{11} = \frac{26}{1}$$

Step 2: Compare the rates.
$$\frac{27}{1} = 27 \text{ students per class} \qquad \frac{26}{1} = 26 \text{ students per class}$$

Solution: **Cleveland High School has 1 more student per class than Garfield.**

EXAMPLE 3

Two numbers are in the ratio 4:7. The difference between them is 9. Find the numbers.

Strategy: **Use Key Concept 1.**

Step 1: Use variables to define the numbers.

Notice: Photocopying any part of this book is forbidden by law.

Let $4x$ = the smaller number
Let $7x$ = the larger number

Step 2: Write and solve an equation using the given information.

$$7x - 4x = 9$$
$$3x = 9$$
$$x = 3, \quad 4x = 12 \quad 7x = 21$$

Solution: **The smaller number is 12; the larger number is 21.**

---

2 PROPORTION

EXAMPLE 4

Solve the equation.

$$\frac{7}{9} = \frac{2x + 3}{3x}$$

Strategy: **Use Key Concepts 3 and 4.**

Step 1: Multiply the means and extremes (cross products).
$21x = 18x + 27$

Step 2: Solve the resulting equation.
$$21x = 18x + 27$$
$$3x = 27$$
$$x = 9$$

Step 3: Check your solution.

$$\frac{7}{9} = \frac{2x+3}{3x} \rightarrow \frac{7}{9} = \frac{2(9)+3}{3(9)} \rightarrow \frac{21}{27} = \frac{7}{9} \checkmark$$

Solution: **In the given equation, $x = 9$.**

EXAMPLE 5

The denominator of a fraction is 3 more than twice the numerator. If 1 is subtracted from the numerator and 2 is added to the denominator, the value of the new fraction is $\frac{1}{3}$. Find the original fraction.

Strategy: **Use Key Concept 4.**

Step 1: Use a variable to define the numerator and denominator of the original fraction.
Let x = the numerator, so $x - 1$ = the new numerator.

Step 2:

Let $2x + 3$ = the denominator,
so $(2x + 3) + 2 = 2x + 5$ = the new denominator.

Write and solve an equation.

$$\frac{x - 1}{2x + 5} = \frac{1}{3}$$

$2x + 5 = 3x - 3$ Use cross products.
$5 = x - 3$
$8 = x$, the original numerator and
$2x + 3 = 2(8) + 3 = 19$, the original denominator.

Solution: **The original fraction is $\frac{8}{19}$; the new fraction is $\frac{7}{21}$, which is equivalent to $\frac{1}{3}$.**

---

3   PERCENT

EXAMPLE 6

What is 0.6% of 140?

Strategy: **Use Key Concepts 3, 4, and 5.**

Step 1: Look carefully at 0.6%. It is not the same as 6%. It is less than 1%. Write the percent as a fraction with a denominator of 100: $\frac{0.6}{100}$

Step 2: Write and solve a proportion.

$$\frac{0.6}{100} = \frac{x}{140}$$

$100x = 84$ Cross multiply.
$x = 0.84$

Solution: **0.6% of 140 = 0.84**

EXAMPLE 7

48 is what percent of 20?

Strategy: **Same as Example 6.**

Step 1: Think about the size of the answer: 48 is greater than 20. Therefore, the answer will be greater than 100%.

Step 2: Write the unknown percent as a fraction: $\frac{x}{100}$.

Step 3: Write and solve a proportion. Be sure the proportion is written so that the solution will be greater than 100%.

$$\frac{48}{20} = \frac{x}{100}$$

$$20x = 48(100)$$
$$20x = 4,800$$
$$x = 240$$

Solution: **48 is 240% of 20.**

EXAMPLE 8

15 is 12% of what number?

Strategy: **Same as Example 6.**

Step 1: Recognize that the answer will be greater than 15 since 15 is a small part (12%) of the answer.

Step 2: Write the percent as a fraction: $\frac{12}{100}$

Step 3: Write and solve a proportion. Be sure the proportion is written so that the solution will be greater than 15.

$$\frac{15}{x} = \frac{12}{100}$$

$$12x = 1500$$
$$x = 125$$

Solution: **15 is 12% of 125.**

EXAMPLE 9

Shawn can bench press 180 pounds, or 120% of his body weight. How much does he weigh?

Strategy: **Same as Example 6.**

Step 1: Recognize that the answer will be less than 180 since 180 is more than 100% of his weight.

Step 2: Write the percent as a fraction: $\frac{120}{100}$

Step 3: Write and solve a proportion.

$$\frac{180}{x} = \frac{120}{100}$$

$$120x = 180(100)$$

$$120x = 18,000$$
$$x = 150$$

Solution: **Shawn weighs 150 lb.**

EXAMPLE 10 What is the amount of sales tax on $550 television if the rate is 6.5%? What is the total cost?

Strategy: **Same as Example 6.**

Step 1: Write a ratio to represent the amount of sales tax.

$$\frac{6.5}{100}$$

Step 2: Write and solve an equation from the data.

$$\frac{6.5}{100} = \frac{x}{550}$$

$$100x = 3575$$
$$x = 35.75$$

Step 3: Find the total cost.
Add the price and the sales tax: $550 + $35.75 = $585.75

Solution: **The amount of sales tax on the television is $35.75, and the total cost is $585.75.**

This problem can also be solved using an equation as follows:
Amount of sales tax = original price × sales tax rate = 550 × 0.065 = $35.75

EXAMPLE 11 After a reduction of 40%, a coat sells for $90. What was its original price?

Strategy: **Same as Example 6.**

Step 1: Use an equation as described above.
Let x = the original price.
Selling price = original price – 40% of the original price
$$90 = x - 0.40x$$
$$90 = 0.60x$$
$$150 = x$$

Solution: **The original price of the coat was $150.**

REGENTS MATH PRACTICE

1. The measures of the two acute angles of a right triangle are in the ratio 8:7. Find the measure of each angle of the triangle.

2. The ratio of two sides of a rectangle is 3:2. If the perimeter of the rectangle is 40 cm, explain how you would find the length of each side of the figure.

3. Carly prepared 28 sandwiches for a class picnic in 45 minutes. Elizabeth did 16 in 24 minutes. Which girl worked at a faster rate? Explain how you know.

4. Two numbers are in the ratio 9:5. The sum of the numbers is 98. Find the two numbers.

5. Solve for the value of x.

$$\frac{5}{x+9} = \frac{6}{3x}$$

6. What number must be subtracted from both the numerator and denominator of $\frac{13}{25}$ so that the resulting fraction is equivalent to $\frac{2}{5}$?

7. What number is 1.7% of 80?

8. To the nearest whole number, what percent of 245 is 100?

9. 90 is what percent of 40?

10. 24 is 15% of what number?

11. Steven Barber's salary is 140% of what it was 4 years ago. If his salary 4 years ago was $30,000, what is his salary today?

12. A store takes 25% off the $160 price of a pair of skates. If another 25% is taken off a week later, what is the total percent discount? Explain why the answer is not 50%.

13. Following a party in a restaurant, the check was $1,350. If 15% of that amount was left as a tip, what was the total cost of the party?

14. If the amount of sales tax paid on the purchase of a $23,250 car is $1,278.75, what is the tax rate?

15. After a price reduction of $10, a jacket is being sold for $40. What was the percent reduction in the price?

LESSON ③⓪
DIRECT VARIATION

KEY CONCEPTS YOU'LL NEED IN THIS LESSON

1. When the ratio of two quantities is always constant, the quantities show **direct variation**.

Cars (x)	1	2	3	9
Tires in use (y)	4	8	12	36

The ratio in the table is always $\frac{1}{4}$: $\frac{1}{4} = \frac{1}{4}$, $\frac{2}{8} = \frac{1}{4}$, $\frac{3}{12} = \frac{1}{4}$, $\frac{9}{36} = \frac{1}{4}$

When you compare y to x, the ratio is always 4.

$$\frac{y}{x} = 4$$

2. If you write the above equation as a proportion, the rule for direct variation can be written as follows

$$\frac{y}{x} = \frac{4}{1}$$

$$y = 4x$$

In general, the rule is $y = kx$ where k is the **constant of variation**.

① VARIATION

EXAMPLE 1 **The table shows the relationship between the number of weeks and the number of days.**

weeks (x)	1	2	3	6	10	13
days (y)	7	14	21	42	70	[ ]

a. **Explain how the table shows constant variation.**
b. **Find the constant of variation.**
c. **Find the missing value in the table.**

Strategy: **Use Key Concepts 1 and 2.**

Step 1: Explain the relationship. The table shows constant variation because in each column, there is a fraction equivalent to $\frac{1}{7}$.

Step 2: Find the constant of variation.
Use the rule $y = kx$. Substitute values from any column.
For example, use $x = 2$ and $y = 14$.

$$y = kx$$
$$14 = k(2) \quad \text{or} \quad 14 = 2k$$
$$k = \frac{14}{2} = 7, \text{ the constant of variation.}$$

Step 3: Find the missing value in the table.
Use the rule $y = kx$ with $k = 7$.
$$y = kx$$
$$y = 7x$$
$$y = 7(13) = 91, \text{ the missing value.}$$

EXAMPLE 2

A printer can print 18 pages in 3 minutes. At that rate, how many pages can it print in 11 minutes?

Strategy: **Use Key Concepts 1 and 2.**

Step 1: Find the constant of variation, k.

$$\frac{y}{x} = \frac{18}{3}$$

$$3y = 18x$$
$$y = 6x, \text{ so } k = 6$$

Step 2: Substitute known values into the rule $y = kx$.
$$y = kx$$
$$y = 6x$$
$$y = 6(11) = 66$$

Solution: **In 11 minutes, the printer can print 66 pages.**

Alternate Solution

Write a proportion using the given values. Let p = the number of pages printed in 11 minutes.

$$\frac{18}{3} = \frac{p}{11}$$

$$3p = 198$$
$$p = 66$$

REGENTS MATH PRACTICE

In problems 1–5, the first variable varies directly as the second. Find the constant of variation.

1. $a = 8, b = 32$

2. $g = 1.5, h = 7.5$

3. $x = 3, y = 1.5$

4. $r = 7, s = 10.5$

5. $m = 16, n = 6$

In problems 6–8, determine whether the values in the table show direct variation. If they do, name the constant of variation. If the do not, give the reason.

6.
j	7	14	35	42
k	4	8	20	24

7.
n	3	5	6	7
p	4	6	7	8

8.
x	8	12	28	36
y	10	15	35	45

9. Traveling at a constant rate, a train covers 135 miles in 3 hours. At the same rate, how far will the train travel in 5 hours?

10. A restaurant has seating for 52 customers at 13 tables, all the same size. If the restaurant expands so that 72 customers can be seated, how many tables will be needed?

LESSON 31
SIMILARITY

KEY CONCEPTS YOU'LL NEED IN THIS LESSON

1. Polygons are **similar** if they have the same shape, but are not necessarily the same size.

2. Polygons have the same shape if:
   - The measures of all pairs of corresponding angles are equal, and
   - The measures of all pairs of corresponding sides form equal ratios (are in proportion).

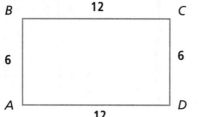

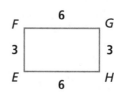

Rectangle *ABCD* ~ Rectangle *EFGH* because
   a. All pairs of corresponding angles are congruent (all are right angles), and
   b. All pairs of corresponding sides form equal ratios:

$$\frac{AD}{EH} = \frac{12}{6} = 2 \qquad \frac{AB}{EF} = \frac{6}{3} = 2 \qquad \frac{BC}{FG} = \frac{12}{6} = 2 \qquad \frac{CD}{GH} = \frac{6}{3} = 2$$

3. Triangles are similar if 3 angles of one are congruent to 3 angles of another.

4. The **ratio of similitude** for two similar polygons is the ratio of the lengths of any pair of sides. In the figures above, the ratio of similitude is 2.

5. In similar polygons, the ratio of perimeters is equal to the ratio of any pair of corresponding sides.

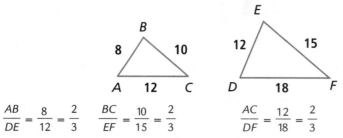

$$\frac{AB}{DE} = \frac{8}{12} = \frac{2}{3} \qquad \frac{BC}{EF} = \frac{10}{15} = \frac{2}{3} \qquad \frac{AC}{DF} = \frac{12}{18} = \frac{2}{3}$$

The ratio of perimeters of △*ABC* to △*DEF* is $\frac{2}{3}$.

6. In similar polygons, the ratio of areas is equal to the ratio of the **square** of any pair of corresponding sides. In the triangles above, the ratio of any pair of corresponding sides is $\frac{2}{3}$.

So, the ratio of the areas is

$$\frac{\text{Area of } \triangle ABC}{\text{Area of } \triangle DEF} = \left(\frac{2}{3}\right)^2 = \frac{2}{3} \times \frac{2}{3} = \frac{4}{9}$$

7. Shadows create similar triangles and can be used to solve indirect measurement problems.

The tree, its shadow, and an imaginary line from the top of the tree to the end of the its shadow form a triangle. A similar triangle is formed by the girl, her shadow, and an imaginary line from the top of her head to the end of her shadow.

---

1 UNDERSTANDING SIMILARITY

EXAMPLE 1

$m\angle D \cong m\angle G$
$m\angle E \cong m\angle H$
$m\angle F \cong m\angle J$

a. **What is the ratio of EF to HJ?**
b. **What is the ratio of similitude of the figures?**
c. **If EF = 18, find the perimeter of △GHJ.**

Strategy: **Use Key Concepts 2, 3, 4, and 5.**

Step 1: Find the ratio of EF to HJ.
The triangles are similar, so corresponding sides form equal ratios.

$$\frac{DF}{GJ} = \frac{10}{5} = \frac{2}{1}, \text{ so } \frac{EF}{HJ} = \frac{2}{1}$$

Step 2: Find the ratio of similitude.
Use any known pair of corresponding sides.

$$\frac{DF}{GJ} = \frac{2}{1}, \text{ so the ratio of similitude is } \frac{2}{1}.$$

Step 3: Find the perimeter of △GHJ.

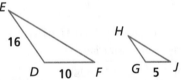

$$\frac{\text{Perimeter of } \triangle DEF}{\text{Perimeter of } \triangle GHJ} = \frac{\text{Side of } \triangle DEF}{\text{Corresponding side of } \triangle GHJ} = \frac{10}{5} = \frac{2}{1}$$

If $EF = 18$, the perimeter of $\triangle DEF = 44$ units and

$\dfrac{44}{x} = \dfrac{2}{1}$ where x = the perimeter of $\triangle GHJ$

$2x = 44$

$x = 22$, the perimeter of $\triangle GHJ$

EXAMPLE 2

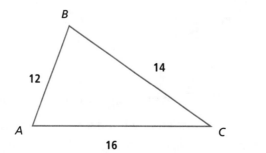

A triangle has sides with lengths 12, 14, and 16. The perimeter of a similar triangle is 21. Find the length of the longest side of the smaller triangle.

Strategy: **Use Key Concepts 2 and 5.**

Step 1:   Find the perimeter of the larger triangle.
$12 + 14 + 16 = 42$

Step 2:   Write and solve a proportion to find the longest side of the smaller

triangle: $\dfrac{\text{Perimeter of larger triangle}}{\text{Perimeter of smaller triangle}} = \dfrac{\text{Longest of larger triangle}}{\text{Longest of smaller triangle}}$

$\dfrac{42}{21} = \dfrac{16}{x}$

$42x = 336$

$x = 8$

Solution: **The longest side of the smaller triangle is 8 units.**

EXAMPLE 3   **For the triangles described in Example 2, what is the ratio of their areas?**

Strategy: **Use Key Concept 6.**

Step 1:   Write the ratio of a pair of corresponding sides.
$\dfrac{AC}{DF} = \dfrac{16}{8} = \dfrac{2}{1}$

Step 2:   Find the ratio of the squares of the sides.

$$\frac{\text{Area of } \triangle ABC}{\text{Area of } \triangle DEF} = \left(\frac{2}{1}\right)^2 = \frac{4}{1}$$

Solution: **The ratio of areas of $\triangle ABC$ to $\triangle DEF$ is 4 to 1.**

---

2 APPLYING SIMILARITY

EXAMPLE 4

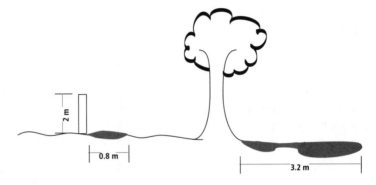

**The 2-meter stick casts 0.8-meter shadow.
At the same time, a nearby tree casts a 3.2-meter shadow. Find the height of the tree.**

Strategy: **Use Key Concept 7.**

Step 1:   Write and solve a proportion that includes the 3 known lengths and the missing length.

$\frac{2}{x} = \frac{0.8}{3.2}$ where x is the height of the tree

$0.8x = 6.4$
$x = 8$

Solution: **The tree is 8 m tall.**

REGENTS MATH PRACTICE

1. Are all squares similar? Explain your reasoning.

2. A rectangular picture frame is 9 in. long by 12 in. wide. A picture to be put in the frame is 6 in. long. If the picture and frame are similar rectangles, how wide is the picture?

3. $\overline{VW}$ is parallel to $\overline{RT}$. Explain how you could demonstrate that $\triangle RST \sim \triangle VSW$.

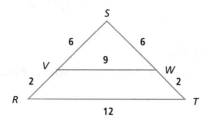

4. Triangle *ABC* has side lengths 12, 18, and 24. Triangle *DEF* has a perimeter of 36. Find the length of the shortest side of triangle *DEF*.

5. In parallelogram *WXYZ*, side *WX* measures 9 cm and side *XY* measures 15 cm. If the lengths of all sides are doubled, what is the ratio of the perimeter of the new figure to the original?

6. Right triangles *JKL* and *MNP* are similar. *JK* = 48 and leg *JL* = 14. Leg *MN* = 24. Find the length of leg *MP*.

7. The building casts a 42 foot shadow at the same time that the boy casts a shadow. Find the length of the boy's shadow to the nearest tenth of a foot.

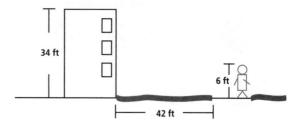

8. *QR* || *TV*   *SV* = 75 ft
   TV = 120 ft   *QS* = 190 ft

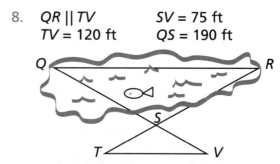

   a. Explain why $\triangle QRS \sim \triangle VTS$.
   b. Find the length of *QR*, the distance across the lake to the nearest foot.

9. *ABCDEF* and *HIJKLM* are regular hexagons. *AB* = 2 cm, *HI* = 5 cm. What is the ratio of the areas of the hexagons?

10. A 35 ft tree casts a 50 ft shadow. At the same time, a girl casts a 6 ft shadow. How much taller than the girl is the tree?

LESSON 32
SPECIAL RIGHT TRIANGLES

KEY CONCEPTS YOU'LL NEED IN THIS LESSON

1. In a right triangle, if the two acute angles measure 30° and 60°, the following relationships apply:

   - If the shortest side of the triangle, the side opposite the 30° angle has a measure of x, then the side opposite the 60° angle has a measure of $x\sqrt{3}$ and the hypotenuse has a measure of $2x$.

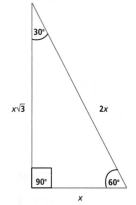

2. In a right triangle, if the measure of each acute angle is 45°, then the following relationships apply:

   - The triangle is isosceles.

   - If the shorter sides each have a measure of x units, then the hypotenuse has a measure of $x\sqrt{2}$ units.

---

1   RIGHT TRIANGLES

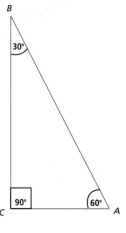

EXAMPLE 1

In right triangle *ABC*, the measure of angle *A* is 60° and the length of side *AB* is 12 cm. Find the length of sides *AC* and *BC* in radical form and to the nearest tenth of a unit.

Strategy: **Use Key Concept 1.**

Step 1: Find the lengths of the other sides in terms of the hypotenuse, *AB*.
The length of the hypotenuse is twice the length of the shortest side, *AC*.
If the hypotenuse is 12, side *AC* must be 12 ÷ 2 or 6.
If the hypotenuse is 12, side *BC* must be the product of the shortest side and $\sqrt{3}$.
So, side *BC* = $6\sqrt{3}$.

Step 2: Find the length of each leg to the nearest tenth of a unit.
Side *AC* = 6.

Side $BC = 6\sqrt{3}$
Use 1.73 as an estimate for $\sqrt{3}$.
Side $BC \approx 6(1.73)$ or about 10.4 units

Solution: **The hypotenuse $AB = 12$, the shorter leg $AC = 6$, and the longer leg $BC = 6\sqrt{3}$ or approximately 10.4.**

EXAMPLE 2

A square garden has a path through it from one corner to the opposite corner. If a side of the square measures 48 ft, how long is the path? Find the answer in radical form and to the nearest tenth of a foot.

Strategy: **Use Key Concept 2.**

Step 1: The diagonal of the square is the hypotenuse of a right triangle formed by the diagonal and two sides of the square. Since the sides are congruent, the triangle is an isosceles right triangle.

Find the length of the diagonal in terms of a side.
Hypotenuse = Side $\times \sqrt{2} = 48\sqrt{2}$ ft in radical form
Use 1.41 as an estimate for $\sqrt{2}$.
Hypotenuse $\approx 48(1.41)$ or about 67.7 ft

Solution: **The length of the diagonal is $48\sqrt{2}$ or approximately 67.7 ft.**

REGENTS MATH PRACTICE

1. In right triangle *ABC*, the measure of acute angle *A* is half the measure of acute angle *B*. The measure of side *AC* is 10 cm. Find the lengths of the other sides of the triangle.

2. Find the length of the hypotenuse in a 30°–60°–90° right triangle in which the longer leg has a measure of $2\sqrt{3}$.

3. A rectangle has side lengths 9 and $9\sqrt{3}$. What is the length of a diagonal if at each vertex it creates complementary angles whose measures are 30° and 60°?

4. The diagonal of a rectangle measures 36 in.
   a. Find the measure of each side of the rectangle if a diagonal forms 30° and 60° angles at opposite vertices.
   b. Find the perimeter of the rectangle.

5. Triangles *RST* and *WXY* are similar with a ratio of similitude of 3. $\overline{RS}$ and $\overline{WX}$ are corresponding sides. What is the length of side *RS* if side *WX* has a measure of $3\sqrt{3}$?

6. In isosceles triangle *MNP*, base angle *M* measures 30° and is congruent to base angle *P*. *NR* is an altitude from point *N* to *MP* and has a measure of 7 cm.

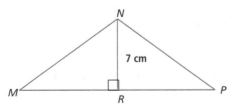

   a. Find the length of $\overline{MR}$.
   b. Find the length of $\overline{MP}$.
   c. Find the length of $\overline{MN}$.

7. The diagonal of a square measures $\sqrt{2}$ m long. What is the
   a. length of a side of the square?
   b. the perimeter of the square?
   c. the area of the square?

8. In an isosceles right triangle, the length of a leg is 8. What is the perimeter of the triangle?

9. In isosceles trapezoid *WXYZ*, the measures of angles *W* and *Z* are each 45°. The lengths of the bases are 10 and 22 cm. Find

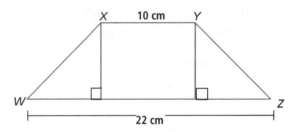

   a. the length of an altitude from *X* to side *WZ*
   b. the length of side *WX*
   c. the perimeter of the trapezoid
   d. the area of the trapezoid

10. In isosceles right triangle *ABC*, the measure of *AC* = 15. $\overline{DE}$ is parallel to $\overline{AC}$ and the ratio of $\overline{AB}$ to $\overline{BD}$ is 3:2.

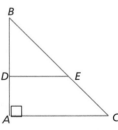

   a. Find the length of $\overline{BC}$.
   b. Find the length of $\overline{BD}$.
   c. Find the length of $\overline{BE}$.
   d. Find the ratio of the area of triangle *ABC* to triangle *DBE*.
   e. Find the area of trapezoid *ADEC*.

LESSON ③③
RIGHT TRIANGLE TRIGONOMETRY

KEY CONCEPTS YOU'LL NEED IN THIS LESSON

1. In right triangles, the longest side is known as the hypotenuse. When a right triangle is known as triangle *ABC*, the right angle is angle *C* and the hypotenuse is side *c*, opposite the right angle.

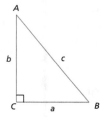

2. In all similar right triangles, the following ratios for either of the corresponding acute angles are always equal:

$$\frac{\text{length of side opposite the angle}}{\text{length of side adjacent to the angle}}$$ (known as the **tangent** ratio, written as tan)

$$\frac{\text{length of side opposite the angle}}{\text{length of hypotenuse}}$$ (known as the **sine** ratio, written as sin)

$$\frac{\text{length of side adjacent to the angle}}{\text{length of hypotenuse}}$$ (known as the **cosine** ratio, written as cos)

3.

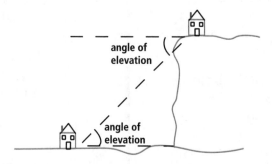

The **angle of elevation** is the angle formed by the horizontal and a line of sight to some elevated position.

The **angle of depression** is the angle formed by the horizontal and a line of sight to a lower position.

For a given situation, the angle of elevation and the angle of depression are congruent.

1 TANGENT RATIO

EXAMPLE 1 **Find the value of the tangent ratio for angle A.**

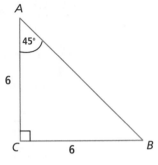

Strategy: **Use Key Concepts 1 and 2.**

Step 1: Write the tangent ratio as $\dfrac{\text{side opposite } \angle A}{\text{side adjacent to } \angle A}$

Step 2: Substitute the lengths of the sides.
$\tan A = \dfrac{6}{6} = 1$

Solution: **For any right triangle with a 45° angle, the value of tan 45° = 1.**

EXAMPLE 2 **In right triangle ABC, m∠A = 60° and side AC = 15. Find side BC to the nearest whole number.**

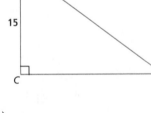

Strategy: **Same as above.**

Step 1: Write the tangent ratio for angle A.

$\tan 60° = \dfrac{\text{opposite}}{\text{adjacent}} = \dfrac{BC}{AC}$

Step 2: Substitute the known values.

$1.7321 = \dfrac{BC}{15}$ (Find tan 60° from your calculator and round to 4 places.)

Step 3: Solve for BC.
$BC = 1.7321(15) = 25.9815$

Solution: **To the nearest whole number, side BC = 26.**

Alternate Solution

Use what you know about the sides in a 30°-60°-90° triangle.
AC is the shorter leg, and BC is the longer leg.
So, BC = AC $\sqrt{3}$ = 15 $\sqrt{3}$ ≈ 25.9808 ≈ 26

---

2 SINE RATIO

EXAMPLE 3

Find the value of the sine ratio for angle A in the triangle .

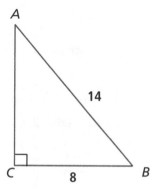

Strategy: Same as above.

Step 1: Write the sine ratio as $\dfrac{\text{side opposite } \angle A}{\text{hypotenuse}}$

Step 2: Substitute the lengths of the sides.

$\sin A = \dfrac{8}{14} \approx 0.5714$

Solution: The value of $\sin A$ is approximately 0.5714.

EXAMPLE 4

A telescope on the ground is aimed at a point on a mountain top. The angle of elevation of the top of the mountain is 68°. The distance from the telescope to the point on the mountain top is 2,875 ft. Find the height of the mountain to the nearest foot.

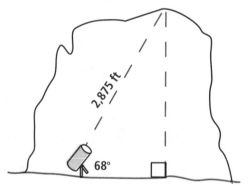

Strategy: Use Key Concept 3.

Step 1: Write the sine ratio for the angle.

$\sin 68° = \dfrac{\text{opposite}}{\text{hypotenuse}}$

Step 2: Find sin 68° on your calculator and round to four places. Substitute the known values.

$0.9272 = \dfrac{x}{2,875}$ Let x = the height of the mountain.

Step 3: Solve for x.
$x = 0.9272(2,875) = 2,665.7$

Solution: To the nearest whole number, the height of the mountain is 2,666 ft.

3   COSINE RATIO

EXAMPLE 5   Find the value of the cosine ratio for angle A in the triangle.

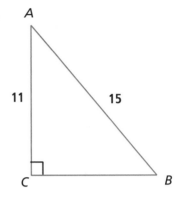

Strategy: Use Key Concept 2.

Step 1:   Write the cosine ratio as $\frac{\text{side adjacent } \angle A}{\text{hypotenuse}}$

Step 2:   Substitute the lengths of the sides.

$\cos A = \frac{11}{15} \approx 0.7333$

Solution: The value of cos A is approximately 0.7333.

EXAMPLE 6   A ranger spots a forest fire from the top of a lookout post that is 120 ft high . The angle of depression of the fire is 40°. To the nearest foot, how far is the fire from the ranger's position at the top of the tower?

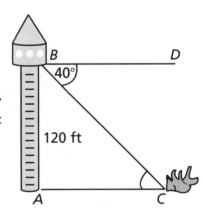

Strategy: Use Key Concept 3.

Step 1:   Find the measure of angle ABC.

Since $m\angle DBC = 40°$, and $\angle DBC$ and $\angle ABC$ are complementary, it follows that $m\angle ABC = 50°$.

Step 2:   Use the cosine ratio to find the distance from the top of the tower to the fire.

$\cos ABC = \frac{BA}{BC}$

$\cos 50° = \frac{120}{BC}$

$0.6428 = \frac{120}{BC}$

$BC \approx 186.7$

Solution: To the nearest foot, the fire is 187 ft from the top of the tower.

REGENTS MATH PRACTICE

Round each answer to the nearest thousandth.

1. Triangle *ABC* is an isosceles right triangle in which $m\angle C = 90°$. Find the value of tan *B*. Explain why the tangent ratio will have this value in any isosceles right triangle.

2. A 62-ft-tall tree is standing near a house. The angle of elevation of the tree top from the house is 37°. If the tree falls, can it hit the house? Explain how you decided.

3. Find the value of cos *A* in right triangle *ABC* in which the measure of angle *A* is 51°.

4. Find the measure of angle *S* in right triangle *RST* to the nearest degree if $m\angle R = 90°$, $RT = 5$ and $ST = 8$.

5. A highway descends at a constant rate of 7° with the horizontal. How many feet does the highway drop between two markers that are 500 feet apart?

6. From a point on a bridge 100 ft above the water, the angle of elevation of the top of a suspension tower is 15°. The horizontal distance from that point to the tower is 520 ft. To the nearest foot, how far above the water does the tower rise?

7. From the top of a mountain 850 ft high, a photographer spots a deer in the valley below. The angle of depression of the deer is 24°. Find the distance from the photographer to the deer.

8. A flagpole casts a shadow 67 ft long when the angle of elevation of the sun is 31°. To the nearest foot, how high is the flag pole?

9. A parallelogram has sides that measure 60 cm and 76 cm. The angle between two sides is 63°. Find the area of the parallelogram to the nearest cm. (*Hint: First find the length of an altitude to a side.*)

10. The diagonal of a rectangle is 24 cm long and intersects a side at an angle of 35°. Find the length and width of the rectangle to the nearest cm.

UNIT ⑥ REVIEW

1. The cost of a lamp, including tax was $27. If the tax rate was 8%, what was the cost of the lamp without tax?

2. The denominator of a fraction is 3 more than the numerator. If the numerator is doubled and the denominator is doubled and then increased by 4, the new fraction is equal to $\frac{1}{2}$. What is the original fraction?

3. A recipe serving 8 people uses 12 eggs. How many people can be served if the recipe is increased so that 30 eggs are used?

4. A living room in the shape of a rectangle is 20 ft long by 12 ft wide. A rectangular area rug for the room is similar to the room. If the rug is 16 ft long, how wide is it?

5. A tree casts a 46 ft shadow at the same time that a $5\frac{1}{2}$ ft tall girl casts a 7 ft shadow. Find the height of the tree to the nearest foot.

6. In parallelogram ABCD, AD = 30 cm and an altitude from vertex B to side AD measures 12 cm. If the length of the base and altitude are both doubled,
   a. What is the new area?
   b. How does the new area compare to the original area?

7. A triangular section of a roof support is in the shape of a right triangle. The measure of angle T is 30° and RS is 16 ft. Find the length of RT. Write the answer in radical form and to the nearest tenth of a foot.

8. A standard karate mat is a square 26 ft on a side. What is the length of a diagonal of the mat? Write the answer in radical form and to the nearest tenth of a foot.

9. A bridge climbs at a constant rate of 5° with the horizontal. To the nearest tenth of a foot, how many feet does the bridge rise between two points that are 650 ft apart?

10. From a telescope 4 ft above the ground, the angle of elevation of the top of a tree is 68°. If the telescope is 105 ft from the base of the tree, how high is the tree, to the nearest foot?

LESSON 34
SOLVING AND GRAPHING LINEAR EQUATIONS

KEY CONCEPTS YOU'LL NEED IN THIS LESSON

[Note: You may wish to refer to Lesson 25 for a quick review of location and distance on the coordinate plane.]

1. A **linear equation in two variables** is an equation whose graph is a straight line.

2. For a linear equation such as $x + 2y = 12$, there are an infinite number of (x, y) pairs (**solutions**) that will make the equation true (**satisfy the equation**).

3. If an ordered pair makes the equation true, it is a solution of the equation. For the equation $x + 2y = 12$, $(6, 3)$ is a solution because $6 + 2(3) = 12$.

4. To **graph** (draw the graph of) a linear equation in two variables, it may be helpful to first solve the equation for y in terms of x. Then you can choose several values of x and find the corresponding values of y.

$$x + 2y = 12$$
$$2y = 12 - x$$
$$y = 6 - \frac{x}{2} \rightarrow$$

x	$6 - \frac{x}{2}$	y	(x, y)
0	$6 - \frac{0}{2}$	6	$(0, 6)$
2	$6 - \frac{2}{2}$	5	$(2, 5)$
4	$6 - \frac{4}{2}$	4	$(4, 4)$

The points $(0, 6)$, $(2, 5)$, and $(4, 4)$ are all solutions to the equation $x + 2y = 12$.

To draw the graph, locate the points on the coordinate plane that are solutions and draw the line that passes through all the points.

5. The **y-intercept** of a line is the point at which the graph of the line crosses the y-axis. The **x-intercept** is the point at which the graph crosses the x-axis.

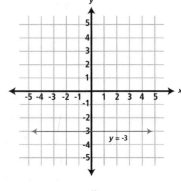

For a line parallel to the x-axis, the y-coordinate will always be the same. For the first graph shown, the y-coordinate will always be -3 and the equation of the line is $y = -3$.

For any line parallel to the x-axis, the equation is $y = a$ where a is the y-intercept.

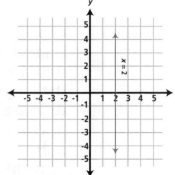

For a line parallel to the y-axis, the x-coordinate will always be the same. For the graph shown, the x-coordinate will always be 2 and the equation of the line is $x = 2$. For any line parallel to the y-axis, the equation is $x = b$ where b is the x-intercept.

6. When two variables show direct variation, their relationship can be shown as a linear graph.

---

1 **SOLUTION SETS OF LINEAR EQUATIONS**

EXAMPLE 1 **Is (-2, 5) a solution to the equation $2x + 9 = y$?**

Strategy: **Use Key Concepts 2 and 3.**

Step 1: Substitute the x and y values into the equation.

$2(-2) + 9 = 5$?

$-4 + 9 = 5$?

$5 = 5$ ✔

Solution: **Since (-2, 5) makes the equation true, it is a solution and the point for (-2, 5) lies on the graph of the equation $2x + 9 = y$.**

EXAMPLE 2 **Find 3 members of the solution set of the equation $2y - 6x = 8$. Then graph the equation.**

Strategy: **Use Key Concepts 2, 3, and the first part of 4.**

Step 1: Solve the equation for y.

$2y - 6x = 8$

$2y = 8 + 6x$

$y = 4 + 3x$ or $y = 3x + 4$

Step 2: Make a table of values:

x	$3x + 4$	y	(x, y)
0	$3(0) + 4$	4	$(0, 4)$
1	$3(1) + 4$	7	$(1, 7)$
2	$3(2) + 4$	10	$(2, 10)$

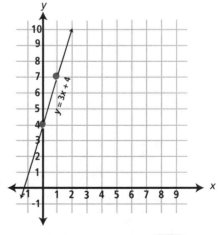

Step 3: Graph the equation. Locate the three points on the coordinate plane. Draw a line that passes through all three points. Label the graph.

Solution: **Every point that lies on the graph of the equation is a solution of the equation.**

2   GRAPHS OF LINES PARALLEL TO THE AXES

EXAMPLE 3

On the same set of axes, draw the graphs of the equations $y = 2$ and $x = -3$.

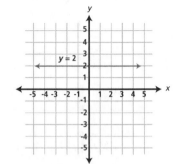

Strategy: **Use Key Concept 5.**

Step 1:   Recognize that the first equation has the form $y = a$ and that $a = 2$.

Step 2:   Draw the graph so that the y-intercept is 2 and the graph is parallel to the x-axis.

Step 3:   Recognize that the second equation has the form $x = b$ and that $b = -3$.

Step 4:   Draw the graph so that the x-intercept is -3 and the graph is parallel to the y-axis.

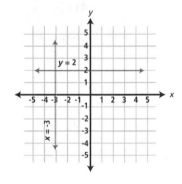

3   GRAPHING DIRECT VARIATION

EXAMPLE 4

During a workout, a runner covers each mile at a steady rate of 8 minutes per mile.
a. What is the constant of variation?
b. Write an equation to show the relationship.
c. Graph the equation.

Strategy: **Use Key Concepts 4 and 6.**

Step 1:   Find the constant of variation.
Recall from Lesson 37 that the constant of variation k is equal to $\frac{y}{x}$.
Set up a table of values.

Number of miles (x)	1	2	3	4	5	6
Number of minutes (y)	8	16	24	32	40	48

The constant of variation $\frac{y}{x} = 8$.

Step 2:   Write an equation for the relationship.
$y = kx \rightarrow y = 8x$ where x is the number of miles run and y is the time in minutes.

Step 3: Graph the equation.
Use a table to find (x, y) values.

x	$8x$	y	(x, y)
1	8(1)	8	(1,8)
2	8(2)	16	(2,16) $\rightarrow$
3	8(3)	24	(3,24)

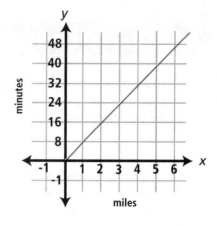

Note the following:

• In this relationship, there are no points in quadrant III. This is because neither the number of miles nor the distance run can be negative.

• The scales for the two axes are not the same. It is only necessary for the scale on each axis to be constant.

REGENTS MATH PRACTICE

1. Is the point (-1, 7) on the graph of the equation $4x + 3 = y$? Explain how you decided.

For problems 2–4, determine the number that must be placed in the frame so that the point will lie on the graph of the equation.

2. $2x - 3y = 12$ (9, [ ])

3. $-3x + y = -1$ (-1, [ ])

4. $7y - x = 4$ ([ ], 2)

5. Complete the table of values for the equation $y = -2x - 3$.

x	-2x – 3	y	(x, y)
0			
1			
2			

In problems 6–10, graph the equation.

6. $y = 2x$

7. $x + y = 5$

8. $x - 3y = 0$

9. $y = 4$

10. $x = -5$

In problems 11 and 12, graph the relationship if the second variable (y) varies directly as the first (x).

11. The cost of lunch (*y*) for 4 people (*x*) is $12

12. There are 15 tennis balls (*y*) in 5 cans (*x*).

LESSON 35 SLOPE

KEY CONCEPTS YOU'LL NEED IN THIS LESSON

1. Slope is a ratio that compares the change in the vertical distance along a line to the change in the horizontal distance, or in the coordinate plane, the difference in y-values divided by the difference in x-values.

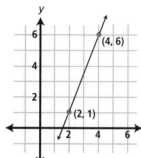

For the line at the left: $\dfrac{\text{difference in } y\text{-values}}{\text{difference in } x\text{-values}} = \dfrac{6-1}{4-2} = \dfrac{5}{2}$

The slope of the line is $\dfrac{5}{2}$.

The order in which you choose the points does not affect the slope: $\dfrac{1-6}{2-4} = \dfrac{-5}{-2} = \dfrac{5}{2}$

2. A line in the coordinate plane is either horizontal, vertical, or oblique (slanted). As you move from left to right
    *   If the line is horizontal, the slope is 0.
    *   If the line rises, the slope is positive.
    *   If the line falls, the slope is negative.

    If the line is vertical, the slope is undefined.

3. A linear equation can be written in the form $y = mx + b$ where m is the slope of the line and b is the y-intercept.

4. In the previous lesson, you reviewed graphing a linear equation by choosing points. A second method of graphing a linear equation is to use the $y = mx + b$ form.
    *   Find and mark the y-intercept, b.
    *   Use the slope, m, to locate other points along the line.
    *   Draw the graph through the points.

5. Parallel lines have equal slopes.

6. Perpendicular lines have slopes that are negative reciprocals of each other. (Negative reciprocals are two numbers whose product is -1.)

7. You can write an equation for a line in slope-intercept form if you know
    *   the slope and a point on the line or
    *   two points on the line

8. You can use the slope of a graph to interpret and solve problems.

1   FINDING SLOPE

EXAMPLE 1

Find the slope of a line that passes through the points $A(1, -4)$ and $B(-3, 2)$.

Strategy: Use Key Concepts 1 and 2.

Step 1: Name $(1, -4)$ as (x_1, y_1) and $(-3, 2)$ as (x_2, y_2)

Step 2: Write the ratio: $\dfrac{y_2 - y_1}{x_2 - x_1} = \dfrac{2 - (-4)}{(-3) - 1} = \dfrac{6}{-4} = -\dfrac{3}{2}$

Solution: The line passing through the points $A(1, -4)$ and $B(-3, 2)$ has slope $-\dfrac{3}{2}$ and slants down from left to right.

EXAMPLE 2

A line that passes through the points $C(0, 3)$ and $D(3, 9)$ is parallel to a line that passes through the points $E(-1, 5)$ and $F(1, w)$. Find the value of w.

Strategy: Use Key Concepts 1 and 5.

Step 1: Find the slope of the line for which you are given two points.

$$\text{slope} = \dfrac{9 - 3}{3 - 0} = \dfrac{6}{3} = \dfrac{2}{1} = 2$$

Since parallel lines have equal slopes, the slope of the second line must be 2.

Step 2: Find the value of w so that the slope of the second line will be 2.

$$\dfrac{w - 5}{1 - (-1)} = 2 \rightarrow \dfrac{w - 5}{2} = 2 \rightarrow w - 5 = 4 \rightarrow w = 9$$

Solution: For the two lines to be parallel, the value of w must be 9.

EXAMPLE 3

Show that a line passing through the points $R(1, 6)$ and $S(2, 8)$ is perpendicular to a line passing through the points $T(3, 7)$ and $V(1, 8)$.

Strategy: Use Key Concepts 1 and 6.

Step 1: Find the slope of each line.

$$\text{slope}_1 = \dfrac{8 - 6}{2 - 1} = \dfrac{2}{1} = 2 \qquad\qquad \text{slope}_2 = \dfrac{8 - 7}{1 - 3} = \dfrac{1}{-2} = -\dfrac{1}{2}$$

Step 2: Demonstrate that 2 and $-\dfrac{1}{2}$ are negative reciprocals.

$$2\left(-\dfrac{1}{2}\right) = -1$$

Solution: Since the slopes of the two lines are negative reciprocals, the lines are perpendicular.

2 GRAPHING A LINEAR EQUATION USING SLOPE AND *y*-INTERCEPT

EXAMPLE 4

Find the slope and *y*-intercept of the equation 3*x* + 2*y* = 8.

Strategy: **Use Key Concept 3.**

Step 1: Write the equation in *y* = *mx* + *b* form.
$3x + 2y = 8$
$2y = 8 - 3x$ Subtract 3*x* from both sides.
$2y = -3x + 8$
$y = \dfrac{-3x}{2} + 4$ Divide both sides by 2.

Step 2: Find the slope and *y*-intercept from the equation.
$y = mx + b$

$y = -\dfrac{3}{2}x + 4$

slope $= -\dfrac{3}{2}$ *y*-intercept = 4 (the point at (0, 4))

Solution: **For the equation 3*x* + 2*y* = 8, the slope is $-\dfrac{3}{2}$ and the *y*-intercept is 4.**

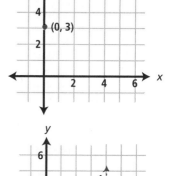

EXAMPLE 4

Draw the graph of the equation 2*y* − *x* = 6 using the slope-intercept method.

Strategy: **Use Key Concept 4.**

Step 1: Write the equation in *y* = *mx* + *b* form.
$2y - x = 6$
$2y = x + 6$

$y = \dfrac{1}{2}x + 3$ slope $= \dfrac{1}{2}$ *y*-intercept = 3

Step 2: Locate the *y*-intercept by graphing, (0, 3) on the coordinate graph.

Step 3: Use the slope to locate two other points that lie along the line.

Step 4: Draw the line that passes through the three points. (Three points are used to help ensure that you have drawn the correct graph.)

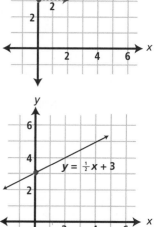

3   WRITING THE EQUATION OF A LINE

EXAMPLE 6

Write an equation of the line that passes through the point with coordinates (1, 4) and has slope -3.

Strategy: Use Key Concepts 3 and 7.

Step 1:   Write the equation $y = mx + b$.
Recall that in the equation, m is the slope of the equation.
Substitute the slope, -3 for m.
$y = -3x + b$

Step 2:   Use the fact that (1, 4) is on the graph of the equation and, therefore, must be a solution to the equation.
Substitute (1, 4) into the equation and solve for b.
$y = -3x + b$
$4 = -3(1) + b$
$4 = -3 + b$
$7 = b$
Substitute 7 for b in the equation.
$y = -3x + 7$

Solution: **An equation of the line that passes through the point with coordinates (1, 4) and has slope 3 is $y = -3x + 7$.**

EXAMPLE 7

Write an equation of the line that passes through the points J (-2, -3) and K (0, 1).

Strategy: Use Key Concepts 1, 3, and 7.

Step 1:   Use the points to find the slope.

Recall that slope, $m = \dfrac{y_2 - y_1}{x_2 - x_1}$

slope $= \dfrac{1 - (-3)}{0 - (-2)} = \dfrac{4}{2} = 2$

Write what you know so far: $y = 2x + b$

Step 2:   Once you know the slope, follow the procedure from Example 6, choosing either point to find b, the y-intercept.
Use K (0, 1).
$y = mx + b$
$1 = 2(0) + b$
$1 = b$

Step 3:	Substitute 1 for b in the equation $y = 2x + b$ $y = 2x + 1$
Solution:	**An equation of the line that passes through the points $J(-2, -3)$ and $K(0, 1)$ is $y = 2x + 1$.**

4 INTERPRETING SLOPE

EXAMPLE 8

The graph represents the distance traveled by a ship over the course of a day.
a. Find the slope of the graph. What does the slope represent?
b. What was the ship's speed in miles per hour?

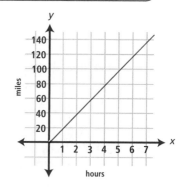

Strategy:	**Use Key Concepts 1 and 8.**
Step 1:	Find the slope. Choose any two points on the graph. Use (3, 60) and (5, 100). slope $= \dfrac{100 - 60}{5 - 3} = \dfrac{40}{2} = 20$
Step 2:	Interpret the slope. Since the slope represents the change in vertical divided by the change in horizontal, write a ratio: slope $= \dfrac{\text{miles traveled}}{\text{number of hours}} = \dfrac{\text{miles}}{\text{hour}}$
Solution:	**The slope of the graph represents the ship's speed in miles per hour. The ship was traveling at a speed of 20 miles per hour.**

REGENTS MATH PRACTICE

In problems 1–4, find the slope of the line passing through the given points. Then describe the line as it moves from left to right.

1. $A(5, 8)$ and $B(10, 6)$

2. $C(-3, 4)$ and $D(5, 12)$

3. $E(9, 7)$ and $F(12, 7)$

4. $G(3, 11)$ and $H(3, -2)$

5. Find the slope of a line that is parallel to a line that passes through $J(10, -2)$ and $K(6, -4)$.

6. Find the slope of a line that is perpendicular to a line that passes through $M(0, 3)$ and $N(6, 1)$.

7. Find the value of x so that the line passing through the points $P(x, 4)$ and $Q(-2, -8)$ has a slope of 3.

8. Demonstrate using slopes that a triangle with vertices at $A(2, 7)$, $B(-1, -5)$ and $C(3, -6)$ is a right triangle. (*Hint: Show that two of the sides are perpendicular by showing that their slopes are the negative reciprocals of each other.*)

9. Demonstrate using slopes that quadrilateral $Q(1, 6)$, $R(4, 5)$, $S(1, -4)$, and $T(-2, -3)$ is a parallelogram. (*Hint: Show that the quadrilateral consists of two pairs of parallel opposite sides.*)

10. What type of parallelogram is figure $QRST$ is problem 9? How do you know?

11. Write the slope and y-intercept of the graph of the equation $5x - 4y = 12$.

12. Write the equation of a line whose graph is parallel to the graph of $y = 3x - 4$.

13. Write the equation of a line whose graph is perpendicular to the graph of $y = -\frac{3}{4}x - 2$.

14. What is the equation of a line whose graph is parallel to the x-axis and 3 units above it?

15. What is the equation of a line whose graph is parallel to the y-axis and 2 units to the left of it?

16. If you know that a graph passes through the origin, what other information do you need to draw the graph of the equation?

17. Draw the graph of $2y = 8 - 4x$.

18. Draw the graph of $y = (\frac{2}{3}x + 1)$

19. Write an equation of the line that passes through the points $W(-1, -1)$ and $Z(3, 4)$.

20. The figure represents the number of miles biked by two students over 3 hours.
    a. Which student is traveling faster?
    b. By how many miles per hour is the faster student traveling than the slower student?

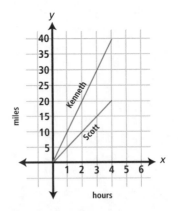

LESSON 36
SYSTEMS OF LINEAR EQUATIONS

1. Two or more equations graphed on the same coordinate plane form a **system**.

   For any two lines drawn, there are three possibilities:
   * The lines may intersect at one point, the solution set for the two equations.
   * The lines may be parallel, in which case they will never intersect and there is no common solution.
   * The lines may have the same graph, in which case every point on the graph(s) is a solution and there are an infinite number of solutions.

   This lesson will focus **consistent equations**, systems of equations that have one solution.

2. A system of equations can be solved graphically by:

   * Graphing each equation, then
   * Noting the point of intersection, and finally by
   * Checking the solution in each original equation.

3a. A system of equations can be **solved algebraically using substitution** by:

   * Substituting one variable for another in one equation, then
   * Solving the resulting one-variable equation, then
   * Using the solution to solve for the other variable, and finally by
   * Checking the solution in each original equation.

3b. A system of equations can be **solved algebraically using addition** by:

   * Making the coefficients of one variable opposites in the two equations, then
   * Eliminating that variable by addition, then
   * Solving the resulting one-variable equation, then
   * Using the solution to solve for the other variable, and finally by
   * Checking the solution in each original equation.

4. Some problems can be solved using two variables and a system of equations by:

   * Representing each unknown by a different variable, then
   * Writing the given relationships as a system of equations, then
   * Solving as in 3a or 3b above, and finally by
   * Checking the solution in the original problem.

1 SOLVING A SYSTEM OF LINEAR EQUATIONS GRAPHICALLY

EXAMPLE 1

Solve graphically and check:
$y - 2 = x$
$2x + 7 = y$

Strategy: **Use Key Concepts 1 and 2, graphing by the slope-intercept method.**

Step 1: Graph the equation $y - 2 = x$.
$y = x + 2$ Add 2 to each side.
        Slope = 1, y-intercept = 2

Step 2: On the same set of axes, graph $2x + 7 = y$
Slope = 2, y-intercept = 7

Step 3: Note the point of intersection.
The graphs intersect at (-5, -3).

Step 4: Check the solution in both original equations.
     $y - 2 = x$ $2x + 7 = y$
   $(-3) - 2 = -5?$ $2(-5) + 7 = -3?$
        $-5 = -5$✔ $-10 + 7 = -3?$
                          $-3 = -3$✔

Solution: **The solution set (point of intersection) of the equations is (-5, -3).**

2 SOLVING A SYSTEM OF LINEAR EQUATIONS USING SUBSTITUTION

EXAMPLE 2

Solve and check:
$x = 3y - 1$
$x - y = 7$

Strategy: **Use Key Concepts 1 and 3a.**

Step 1: Since $x = 3y - 1$, $3y - 1$ can be substituted into the second equation for x, so
$(3y - 1) - y = 7$

Step 2: Solve $(3y - 1) - y = 7$ for y.
   $(3y - 1) - y = 7$
       $2y - 1 = 7$ Remove parentheses and combine like terms.
          $2y = 8$
           $y = 4$

Step 3: Use $y = 4$ to solve for x. Choose either of the original equations that contains both x and y.

Use $x = 3y - 1$
$x = 3(4) - 1$
$x = 12 - 1 = 11$

Step 4:   Check the solution $x = 11$, $y = 4$.

$x = 3y - 1$	$x - y = 7$
$11 = 3(4) - 1?$	$11 - 4 = 7?$
$11 = 11$✔	$11 = 11$✔

Solution: **The solution set is $x = 11$, $y = 4$.**

---

3   **SOLVING A SYSTEM OF LINEAR EQUATIONS USING ADDITION**

EXAMPLE 3

Solve and check:
$3x - 4y = 11$
$5x - 3y = 33$

Strategy: **Use Key Concepts 1 and 3b.**

Step 1:   Eliminate one variable by making the coefficients of that variable either the same or opposites.

The following steps can be used to eliminate the variable x:

$(3x - 4y = 11)(-5) \rightarrow -15x + 20y = -55$ $(3x - 4y = 11)5 \rightarrow 15x - 20y = 55$
$(5x - 3y = 33)3 \rightarrow \underline{15x - 9y = 99}$ **or** $(5x - 3y = 33)(-3) \rightarrow \underline{-15x + 9y = -99}$
$\qquad\qquad\qquad\qquad\quad 11y = 44 \qquad\qquad\qquad\qquad\qquad\qquad -11y = -44$
$\qquad\qquad\qquad\qquad\quad\quad y = 4 \qquad\qquad\qquad\qquad\qquad\qquad\quad\quad y = 4$

Alternately, eliminate the variable y:

$(3x - 4y = 11)3 \rightarrow 9x - 12y = 33$ $(3x - 4y = 11)(-3) \rightarrow -9x + 12y = -33$
$(5x - 3y = 33)(-4) \rightarrow \underline{-20x + 12y = -132}$ **or** $(5x - 3y = 33)4 \rightarrow \underline{20x - 12y = 132}$
$\qquad\qquad\qquad\qquad\quad -11x = -99 \qquad\qquad\qquad\qquad\qquad\qquad 11x = 99$
$\qquad\qquad\qquad\qquad\qquad\quad x = 9 \qquad\qquad\qquad\qquad\qquad\qquad\quad x = 9$

Step 2:   Find the value of the missing variable by substituting the known variable in any equation containing both variables.
Using the equation $3x - 4y = 11$,

If you found $y = 4$, then	If you found $x = 9$, then
$3x - 4(4) = 11$	$3(9) - 4y = 11$
$3x - 16 = 11$	$27 - 4y = 11$
$3x = 27$	$-4y = -16$
$x = 9$	$y = 4$

Solution: **For the given system of equations, the solution is $x = 9$ and $y = 4$.**

USING SYSTEMS OF EQUATIONS TO SOLVE PROBLEMS

EXAMPLE 4

Find the area of the triangle formed by the graphs of the equations $x = -2$, $y = -x$, and $y = -4$.

Strategy: **Use Key Concept 2.**

Step 1: Graph each equation on the same set of axes.

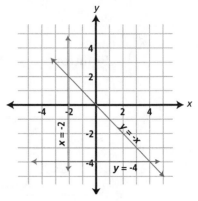

Step 2: Find the area of the resulting triangle.
Use the area formula for a triangle: $A = \frac{bh}{2}$
$b = x_2 - x_1 = 4 - (-2) = 6$
$h = y_2 - y_1 = 2 - (-4) = 6$
$A = \frac{bh}{2} = \frac{6(6)}{2} = \frac{36}{2} = 18$

Solution: **The area of the triangle formed by the graphs of the given equations is 18 units^2.**

EXAMPLE 5

The athletic director of Glenn High School bought 12 basketballs and 7 footballs for a total of $685. The director at Johnson High School paid $599 for 9 basketballs and 8 footballs. What is the cost of one ball of each type?

Strategy: **Use Key Concept 4.**

Step 1: Define each variable.
Let x = the cost of one basketball
Let y = the cost of one football

Step 2: Write and solve a system of equations using the given information.
$12x + 7y = 685$
$9x + 8y = 599$

Eliminate the variable x.
$(12x + 7y = 685)(-3) \rightarrow -36x - 21y = -2{,}055$
$(9x + 8y = 599)4 \quad \rightarrow \underline{36x + 32y = 2{,}396}$
$\phantom{(9x + 8y = 599)4 \quad \rightarrow 36x + {}} 11y = 341$
$\phantom{(9x + 8y = 599)4 \quad \rightarrow 36x + {}} y = 31$

Solve for the other variable, x. Use the equation $12x + 7y = 685$.
$12x + 7(31) = 685$
$12x + 217 = 685$
$12x = 468$
$x = 39$

Step 3: Check the solution, using the two original equations.

$$12x + 7y = 685 \qquad\qquad 9x + 8y = 599$$
$$12(39) + 7(31) = 685 \qquad 9(39) + 8(31) = 599$$
$$468 + 217 = 685 \qquad\qquad 351 + 248 = 599$$
$$685 = 685\checkmark \qquad\qquad 599 = 599\checkmark$$

Solution: **One basketball costs \$39, one football costs \$31.**

EXAMPLE 6

Michael weighs 87 pounds more than his dog. Together Michael and his dog weigh 121 pounds. How much does each weigh?

Strategy: **Use Key Concept 4.**

(*This is an example of a problem that can be solved using either one or two variables. The solution method shown here uses two. In all problems, you should consider all possibilities.*)

Step 1: Define variables.
Let x = Michael's weight
Let y = His dog's weight

Step 2: Write and solve a system of equations using the information in the problem.

$$x - y = 87$$
$$\underline{x + y = 121} \qquad \text{Add the equations to eliminate the variable } y.$$
$$2x = 208$$
$$x = 104$$

Step 3: Use the known value of x to solve for y.

$$x - y = 87$$
$$104 - y = 87$$
$$y = 17$$

Step 4: Check the solution in both equations.

$$x - y = 87 \qquad\qquad x + y = 121$$
$$104 - 17 = 87 \qquad\quad 104 + 17 = 121$$
$$87 = 87\checkmark \qquad\qquad 121 = 121\checkmark$$

Solution: **Michael weighs 104 pounds, his dog weighs 17 pounds.**

REGENTS MATH PRACTICE

In problems 1 and 2, solve the system of equations graphically and check.

1. $y = x + 1$
$-x - y = 7$

2. $x + y = 9$
$2x - y = 3$

In problems 3–6, solve algebraically and check.

3. $5x + 7y = 50$
$9x + 14y = 97$

4. $5x - 7y = -4$
$9x + 11y = 40$

5. $y = 4x$
$5x - 3y = -21$

6. $x = 5y$
$-3x + 4y = 22$

7. Find the area of the triangle formed by the graphs of the equations $y = x$, $y = 3$, and $x = 0$.

In problems 8–12, write and solve a system of linear equations using two variables.

8. The sum of two numbers is 78. One of the numbers is five times the other. Find the numbers.

9. The difference between two numbers is 15. If their sum is 53, find the numbers.

10. The perimeter of a rectangular field is 84 yd. If the length is twice the width, find the dimensions of the field.

11. On Tuesday, Arthur used two phone companies to make long distance calls. Using Northern Phone Company for 16 minutes and Southern for 8 minutes, he paid a total of $2.48. On Wednesday, he used Northern for 14 minutes and Southern for 11 minutes and paid a total of $2.69. What does each company charge per minute of use?

12. An investor bought some shares of stock in two companies. She paid $45 per share for one company and $60 per share for the other. If she bought 40 shares in all and paid a total of $2,175, how many shares did she buy at each price?

LESSON ③⑦
SYSTEMS OF LINEAR INEQUALITIES

KEY CONCEPTS YOU'LL NEED IN THIS LESSON

[*A review of Lesson 17 Inequalities should precede this Lesson.*]

1. An **inequality in two variables**, such as $y \geq 2x + 1$ can be graphed as follows:

   • Graph the **plane divider**, $y = 2x + 1$, using a solid line to account for the fact that the symbol $\geq$ is used (is greater than **or equal to**).

   The plane divider divides the plane into two **half planes**.

   • Determine whether to shade above or below the plane divider by testing a point. If the point satisfies the inequality, shade the half plane containing that point. If the point does not satisfy the inequality, shade the half plane that does not contain the point.

2. When drawing the plane divider or equation, keep the following in mind:

If the inequality symbol is	Graph the equation (plane divider) using
<	A dashed line
>	A dashed line
≤	A solid line
≥	A solid line

3. To graph the solution set of a system of inequalities, follow the above for each inequality. The solution set is the region that satisfies both inequalities. It is shown as the double shaded region when the solution to each inequality is shaded.

---

① SYSTEMS OF LINEAR INEQUALITIES

EXAMPLE 1

Graph the solution set of the system of inequalities:
$y < 2x - 1$
$x + y \geq 3$
Name a point in the solution set.

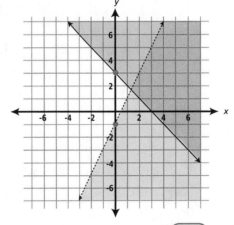

Strategy: Use Key Concepts 1 – 3.

Step 1: Graph $y < 2x - 1$.
Graph the plane divider $y = 2x - 1$, using a dashed line.
Then test any point on either side of the line in the inequality.
Test $(0, 0)$.

Notice: Photocopying any part of this book is forbidden by law.

When $x = 0$ and $y = 0$, the inequality $y < 2x - 1$ becomes

$0 < 2(0) - 1$

$0 < 0 - 1$

$0 < -1$

Since $0 < -1$ is not a true inequality, the point $(0, 0)$ is not in the solution set.

Shade the half-plane that does not contain $(0, 0)$.

Step 2: Repeat Step 1 for $x + y \geq 3$.

Graph the plane divider $x + y = 3$, using a solid line.

Again, test the point $(0, 0)$ in the inequality. Since $(0, 0)$ does not make $x + y \geq 3$ true, shade the half plane that does not contain $(0, 0)$.

Step 3: Name a point in the solution set.

Any (x, y) point that satisfies both inequalities is in the solution set. Any (x, y) point in the double shaded region satisfies both inequalities.

Test $(4, 2)$.

$y < 2x - 1$ $x + y \geq 3$

$2 < 2(4) - 1$ $4 + 2 \geq 3$

$2 < 8 - 1$ $6 \geq 3$ ✔

$2 < 7$ ✔

REGENTS MATH PRACTICE

Graph the solution set of each system of inequalities.

1. $x \leq 2$
   $y > 3$

2. $y \geq 1$
   $x \geq -1$

3. $y \leq x$
   $x + y \geq 0$

4. $y < x + 1$
   $x \leq 0$

5. $-2 < y < 2$

6. $2 < x \leq 5$

Notice: Photocopying any part of this book is forbidden by law.

163

LESSON 38
GRAPHS OF QUADRATIC EQUATIONS

KEY CONCEPTS YOU'LL NEED IN THIS LESSON

1. A quadratic equation in the form $y = ax^2 + bx + c$ can be graphed on the coordinate plane using a table of (x, y) values. If a, b, and c are real numbers and $a \neq 0$, the graph will be a **parabola**.

2. If a is positive, the parabola opens upward. A parabola that opens upward has a **minimum point**.
    If a is negative, the parabola opens downward. A parabola that opens downward has a **maximum point**.

3. The parabola has an **axis of symmetry**. Every point on one side of the graph matches a point on the opposite side. The **equation of the axis of symmetry is** $x = \frac{-b}{2a}$.

    The axis of symmetry always passes through the minimum or maximum point. Since the parabola turns at the minimum or maximum point, that point is also known as the **turning point**.

1 GRAPHS OF QUADRATIC EQUATIONS

EXAMPLE 1 Graph the quadratic equation $y = x^2 + 2x$, using all integer values of x where $-4 \leq x \leq 2$.

Strategy: Use Key Concepts 1 and 2.

Step 1: Recognize that in the equation $y = x^2 + 2x$, a is positive 1. Therefore, the parabola that is the graph will open upward.

Step 2: Set up a table of values using all x values where $-4 \leq x \leq 2$.

x	$x^2 + 2x$	y	(x, y)
-4	$(-4)^2 + 2(-4)$	8	(-4, 8)
-3	$(-3)^2 + 2(-3)$	3	(-3, 3)
-2	$(-2)^2 + 2(-2)$	0	(-2, 0)
-1	$(-1)^2 + 2(-1)$	-1	(-1, -1)
0	$(0)^2 + 2(0)$	0	(0, 0)
1	$(1)^2 + 2(1)$	3	(1, 3)
2	$(2)^2 + 2(2)$	8	(2, 8)

Step 3: Locate the points on a coordinate grid.

Step 4: Draw a smooth curve through the points.

Solution: **The graph of the equation $y = x^2 + 2x$ is a parabola, opening upward as shown.**

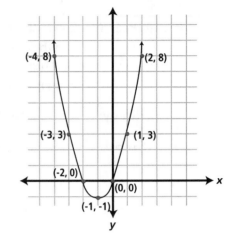

EXAMPLE 2   **Use the graph in Example 1.**
a. Name the minimum point.
b. Write the equation of the axis of symmetry.

Strategy: **Use Key Concepts 2 and 3.**

Step 1: Find the minimum point from either the table or the graph.
The minimum point contains the least y value of all the (x, y) points you found.
From the table, the point with the least y value is (-1, -1).
From the graph, the point where the parabola turns is the minimum point, or (-1, -1).

Step 2: Find the equation of the axis of symmetry.
Use the equation $x = \frac{-b}{2a}$, where $a = 1$ and $b = 2$ (from $y = x^2 + 2x$).

$x = \frac{-2}{2(1)}$

$x = \frac{-2}{2} = -1$

$x = -1$ is the equation of the axis of symmetry.

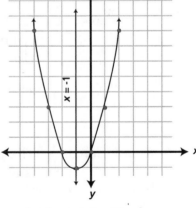

Solution: **For the graph of $y = x^2 + 2x$, the minimum point is at (-1, -1); the equation of the axis of symmetry is $x = -1$.**

EXAMPLE 3

Graph the quadratic equation $y = -x^2 - 1$ for all integer values of x where $-3 \leq x \leq 3$.

Then find the maximum point and the equation of the axis of symmetry.

Strategy: **Use Key Concepts 1, 2, and 3.**

Step 1: Set up a table of values. Since a is negative, the parabola will open downward.

x	$-x^2 - 1$	y	(x, y)
-3	$-(-3)^2 - (1)$	-10	(-3, -10)
-2	$-(-2)^2 - (1)$	-5	(-2, -5)
-1	$-(-1)^2 - (1)$	-2	(-1, -2)
0	$-(0)^2 - (1)$	-1	(0, -1)
1	$-(1)^2 - (1)$	-2	(1, -2)
2	$-(2)^2 - (1)$	-5	(2, -5)
3	$-(3)^2 - (1)$	-10	(3, -10)

Step 2: Locate the points and draw the graph.

Step 3: Find the maximum point of the graph. The maximum point contains the greatest y value. Therefore, the maximum point of the graph is at (0, -1).

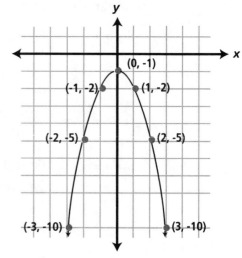

Step 4: Find the equation of the axis of symmetry.
Use the values -1 for a and 0 for b.

$$x = \frac{-b}{2a}$$

$$x = \frac{-(0)}{2(-1)} = \frac{0}{-2} = 0$$

Solution: **The graph of the equation $y = -x^2 - 1$ is shown. The maximum point is at (0, -1), and the equation of the axis of symmetry is $x = 0$.**

Alternate Method: You can find the equation of the axis of symmetry and then use it to find the coordinates of the maximum point.
- For the equation $y = -x^2 - 1$, the equation of the axis of symmetry is found as above: $x = 0$.
- Since the x-coordinate of the maximum point is 0, find the y-coordinate by substituting 0 for x in the equation $y = -x^2 - 1$: $y = -(0)^2 - 1 = 0 - 1 = -1$

Therefore, the coordinates of the maximum point or turning point are (0, -1).

REGENTS MATH PRACTICE

In 1–4, graph the quadratic equation, using all integer values of x as given.

1. $y = 2x^2$ for $-2 \leq x \leq 2$

2. $y = -x^2$ for $-3 \leq x \leq 3$

3. $y = x^2 - 2x + 1$ for $-2 \leq x \leq 4$

4. $y = -x^2 + 1$ for $-3 \leq x \leq 3$

In problems 5–10, determine whether the parabola opens upward or downward. Then find the axis of symmetry and the coordinates of the turning point.

5. $y = x^2 - 9$

6. $y = -2x^2 - 4x + 3$

7. $y = -3x^2 + 6x - 8$

8. $y = x^2 - 6x$

9. $y = x^2 - 2x + 1$

10. $y = -2x^2 + x - 5$

LESSON (39)
QUADRATIC-LINEAR SYSTEMS

KEY CONCEPTS YOU'LL NEED IN THIS LESSON

1. The solution to a system of equations consists of those points that satisfy both equations.

2. A system consisting of a quadratic equation and a linear equation can be solved graphically. Use techniques similar to those used to solve systems of linear equations. However, since the graph of a quadratic equation may be a parabola, a line may intersect the parabola at one point, two points, or no points. If the graphs do not intersect, there are no real number solutions to the system.

3. A system of a quadratic and linear equation may be solved algebraically. Solve for one variable in terms of the other in the linear equation. Then substitute the expression into the quadratic equation and solve. Finally, return to the linear equation to find remaining unknowns.

1 SOLVING A QUADRATIC-LINEAR SYSTEM GRAPHICALLY

EXAMPLE 1

Solve and check: $y = x^2 - 5$ **and** $y = x + 1$.

Strategy: **Use Key Concepts 1 and 2.**

Step 1: Draw the graph of $y = x^2 - 5$.
Find the equation of the axis of symmetry. Then use several x-values on either side of the axis.

$$\text{axis of symmetry} = \frac{-b}{2a} = \frac{0}{2(1)} = 0$$

So, the equation of the axis of symmetry is $x = 0$.

Step 2: Use values of x so that $-3 \leq x \leq 3$.

x	$x^2 - 5$	y	(x, y)
-3	$(-3)^2 - 5$	4	(-3, 4)
-2	$(-2)^2 - 5$	-1	(-2, -1)
-1	$(-1)^2 - 5$	-4	(-1, -4)
0	$(0)^2 - 5$	-5	(0, -5)
1	$(1)^2 - 5$	-4	(1, -4)
2	$(2)^2 - 5$	-1	(2, -1)
3	$(3)^2 - 5$	4	(3, 4)

Step 3: Draw the parabola that is the graph of the equation $y = x^2 - 5$.

Step 4: Draw the graph of $y = x + 1$. Use the slope-intercept method: slope = 1, y-intercept = 1.

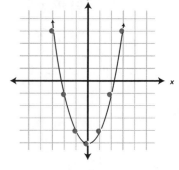

Step 5: Find the solutions. There are two solutions since the graphs intersect at two points.
Solution 1: (3, 4)   Solution 2: (-2, -1)

Step 6: Check each solution in each equation, a total of 4 checks.

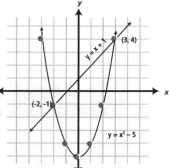

$x = 3, y = 4$		$x = -2, y = -1$	
$y = x^2 - 5$	$y = x + 1$	$y = x^2 - 5$	$y = x + 1$
$4 = (3)^2 - 5$	$4 = 3 + 1$	$-1 = (-2)^2 - 5$	$-1 = -2 + 1$
$4 = 9 - 5$	$4 = 4$ ✔	$-1 = 4 - 5$	$-1 = -1$ ✔
	$4 = 4$ ✔		$-1 = -1$ ✔

Solution: **The solutions to $y = x^2 - 5$ and $y = x + 1$ are at (3, 4) and (-2, -1).**

2 SOLVING A QUADRATIC-LINEAR SYSTEM ALGEBRAICALLY

EXAMPLE 2   **Solve and check: $4x + y = x^2$ and $y = -3x + 6$**

Strategy: **Use Key Concepts 1 and 3.**

Step 1: Substitute $-3x + 6$ for y in the quadratic equation.
$$4x + y = x^2$$
$$4x + (-3x + 6) = x^2$$

Step 2: Transform the quadratic equation into standard form and solve.
$$4x + (-3x + 6) = x^2$$
$$x + 6 = x^2$$
$$x^2 - x - 6 = 0$$
$$(x - 3)(x + 2) = 0$$

$x - 3 = 0$	$x + 2 = 0$
$x = 3$	$x = -2$

Step 3: Substitute each x value into the linear equation to solve for the corresponding value of y.

$y = -3x + 6$	$y = -3x + 6$
$y = -3(3) + 6$	$y = -3(-2) + 6$
$y = -9 + 6$	$y = 6 + 6$
$y = -3$	$y = 12$

Step 4:   Write both solutions: (3, -3) and (-2, 12).

Step 5:   Check each solution in both equations, a total of 4 checks.

$x = 3, y = -3$		$x = -2, y = 12$	
$4x + y = x^2$	$y = -3x + 6$	$4x + y = x^2$	$y = -3x + 6$
$4(3) + (-3) = 3^2$	$-3 = -3(3) + 6$	$4(-2) + 12 = (-2)^2$	$12 = -3(-2) + 6$
$12 + (-3) = 9$	$-3 = -9 + 6$	$-8 + 12 = 4$	$12 = 6 + 6$
$9 = 9$ ✔	$-3 = -3$ ✔	$4 = 4$ ✔	$12 = 12$ ✔

REGENTS MATH PRACTICE

In 1–4, solve each system graphically and check each solution.

1. $y = 2x^2$
    $y = -x + 1$

2. $y = x^2 + 2$
    $y = x + 2$

3. $y = 2x^2 - 3$
    $x + y = 3$

4. $y = -x^2 + 2$
    $y = x$

In 5–10, solve each system algebraically and check each solution.

5. $y = x^2 - x + 2$
    $y = 2x$

6. $y = x^2 - 2$
    $x = y - 4$

7. $y = x^2 - 3x - 6$
    $x + y = 9$

8. $y = x^2 - 7x + 13$
    $x - y = 2$

9. $y = -x^2 - 1$
    $y = x - 3$

10. $y = 2x^2 - 21$
    $x + y = 0$

UNIT **7** REVIEW

1. Is the point (-2, -5) on the graph of the equation $2x + y = -9$? Explain how you decided.

2. The point $(8, y)$ lies on the graph of the equation $x - 2y = 14$. Find the value of y.

3. Find the slope of a line that passes through the points $(-1, 7)$ and $(2, 4)$. Then describe the line as it moves from left to right.

4. Find the equation of a line that is parallel to $y = 3x - 2$ and intersects the y-axis at $(0, 4)$.

5. Find the slope and y-intercept of the graph of the equation $3x + 4y = 6$

In problems 6 and 7, solve the system of equations either graphically or algebraically.

6. $x - y = -5$
   $5x + 4y = 2$

7. $5x^2 - 2x + 1 = y$
   $x - y = -3$

8. Mr. Jones stops at a fast-food take-out each Monday. One week he spent $17.10 for 6 burgers and 4 drinks. The next week, he spent $16.50 for 5 burgers and 5 drinks. Find the cost of one burger and the cost of one drink.

9. Is (8, 3) a solution to the following system of linear inequalities? Explain how you decided.
   $y < x - 4$
   $2y + 2 \geq x$

10. $(-3, y)$ is in the solution set of the following inequalities. Name a possible value of y.
    $2x + 3 < y$
    $-x + 1 > y$

LESSON 40 AREA

KEY CONCEPTS YOU'LL NEED IN THIS LESSON

1. When a triangle or quadrilateral on the coordinate plane has at least one side parallel to an axis, its area can generally be found by using the area formula for the given figure.

2. When a triangle or quadrilateral on the coordinate plane has no sides parallel to an axis, its area can be found by the following steps:

   - Draw a rectangle that encloses the figure. The rectangle should touch the uppermost, lowermost, leftmost, and rightmost point on the figure.

   - Find the area of the rectangle. Find the area of each of the right triangles created inside the rectangle, but outside the given figure. If the rectangle does not create only triangles, it may be necessary to separate an area further into other figures.

   - Subtract the sum of the right triangles formed from the area of the rectangle. What is left is the area of the original figure.

1 AREA

EXAMPLE 1   **Find the area of triangle *QRS*.**

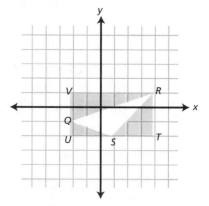

Strategy: **Use Key Concept 2.**

Step 1:   Draw rectangle *RTUV* surrounding the triangle.

Step 2:   Find the area of the rectangle.
$A = bh = 6 \times 3 = 18$

Step 3:   Find the area of each right triangle and the sum of their areas.

Area of right triangle $QVR = \frac{6(2)}{2} = \frac{12}{2} = 6$

Area of right triangle $RST = \frac{3(3)}{2} = \frac{9}{2} = 4.5$

Area of right triangle $QSU = \frac{3(1)}{2} = \frac{3}{2} = 1.5$

Sum of the areas of the right triangles = 6 + 4.5 + 1.5 = 12

Step 4:   Subtract to find the area of triangle QRS.
18 – 12 = 6

Solution: **The area of triangle QRS = 6 units².**

EXAMPLE 2   **Find the area of quadrilateral ABCD.**

Strategy: **Use Key Concept 2, dividing the figure as shown.**

Step 1:   Draw rectangle AFCI.

Step 2:   Find the area of Rectangle AFCI.
$A = bh = 5 \times 6 = 30$

Step 3:   Find the areas of each of the other figures and the sum of their areas.

Area of square BEFG = s^2 = 1 × 1 = 1

Area of square DHIJ = s^2 = 1 × 1 = 1

Area of right triangle ABE = $\dfrac{bh}{2} = \dfrac{1(5)}{2} = 2.5$

Area of right triangle BCG = $\dfrac{bh}{2} = \dfrac{1(4)}{2} = 2$

Area of right triangle CDH = $\dfrac{bh}{2} = \dfrac{1(5)}{2} = 2.5$

Area of right triangle ADJ = $\dfrac{bh}{2} = \dfrac{1(4)}{2} = 2$

Sum of the areas = 1 + 1 + 2.5 + 2 + 2.5 + 2 = 11

Step 4:   Subtract to find the area of the quadrilateral.
30 – 11 = 19

Solution: **The area of quadrilateral ABCD = 19 units².**

REGENTS MATH PRACTICE

Find the area of each figure.

1.

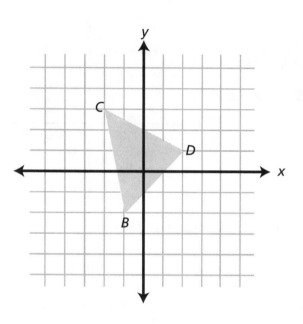

2.

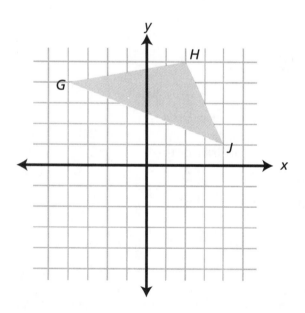

3.

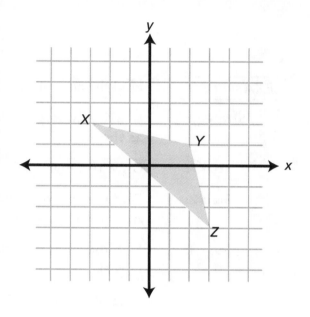

4.

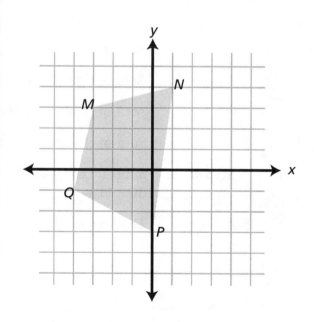

LESSON 41

LINE REFLECTION AND LINE SYMMETRY

KEY CONCEPTS YOU'LL NEED IN THIS LESSON

This lesson and the following one concern themselves with **transformations**. A transformation in the plane is a movement of a point or figure in the plane according to a rule.

1. A **line reflection** can be thought of as creating a mirror image. Each point on the original figure corresponds to a point on the **image**.

2. Together, a figure and its reflection have **line symmetry** about **the reflection line** or **axis of symmetry**.

3. The reflection line is the perpendicular bisector of a line segment connecting any point on the original figure—not on the reflection line—with its image.

4. Certain general rules apply to reflections in the coordinate plane:

    *   If a figure is reflected in the y-axis, every point (x, y) on the figure becomes $(-x, y)$.

    *   If a figure is reflected in the x-axis, every point (x, y) on the figure becomes $(x, -y)$.

    *   If a figure is reflected in the line $y = x$, every point (x, y) on the figure becomes (y, x).

---

1   LINE REFLECTION AND LINE SYMMETRY

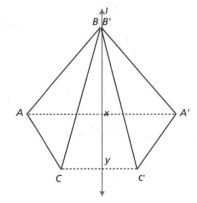

EXAMPLE 1

Figure $A'B'C'$ is the reflection of figure ABC after a reflection in line l.
a. Name the axis of symmetry.
b. Name all congruent segments.
c. Name all right angles.
d. Explain how you would demonstrate that the triangles are congruent.

Strategy: Use Key Concepts 1, 2, and 3.

Step 1:   Identify the axis of symmetry.
The axis of symmetry for the original figure and its image is the reflection line, l.

Step 2: Name all congruent segments.

Since line l bisects the line connecting each point on the original figure with its image, $\overline{AX} = \overline{XA'}$ and $\overline{CY} = \overline{YC'}$. Points B and B' are the same point since B lies on the reflection line.

Step 3: Name all right angles.

Since line l is the perpendicular bisector of $\overline{AA'}$ and $\overline{CC'}$, all angles formed by $\overline{AA'}$ and line l and all angles formed by $\overline{CC'}$ and line l are right angles.

Step 4: Demonstrate that the triangles are congruent.

Trace the figure carefully on a sheet of paper. Fold the paper in half over line l. Do the two figures exactly cover each other? Since they do, they are congruent.

EXAMPLE 2

Triangle *HJK* has the following coordinates: *H*(2, -3), *J*(1, -1), and *K*(4, 2).
Find the coordinates of its image after:
a. a reflection in the *y*-axis
b. a reflection in the *x*-axis
c. a reflection in *y* = *x*

Strategy: **Use Key Concept 4.**

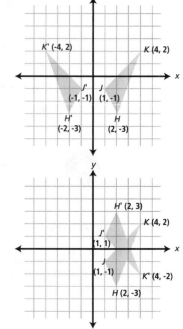

Step 1: Find the coordinates after a reflection in the y-axis. Use the rule: $(x, y) \rightarrow (-x, y)$ for a reflection in the y-axis.

$H(2, -3) \rightarrow H'(-2, -3)$, $J(1, -1) \rightarrow J'(-1, -1)$, and $K(4, 2) \rightarrow K'(-4, 2)$

Step 2: Find the coordinates after a reflection in the x-axis. Use the rule: $(x, y) \rightarrow (x, -y)$ for a reflection in the x-axis.

$H(2, -3) \rightarrow H'(2, 3)$, $J(1, -1) \rightarrow J'(1, 1)$, and $K(4, 2) \rightarrow K'(4, -2)$

Step 3: Find the coordinates after a reflection in $y = x$. Use the rule: $(x, y) \rightarrow (y, x)$ for a reflection in $y = x$.

$H(2, -3) \rightarrow H'(-3, 2)$, $J(1, -1) \rightarrow J'(-1, 1)$, and $K(4, 2) \rightarrow K'(2, 4)$

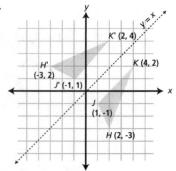

REGENTS MATH PRACTICE

1. Triangle *M'N'P'* is the reflection of triangle *MNP* after a reflection over line *m*. If neither *M*, *N*, nor *P* lie on line *m*, how many pairs of congruent line segments are formed by the reflection?

In problems 2–5, find the image of the given point after a reflection in the given line.

2. (4, 7), *y*-axis

3. (-2, 5), line *y = x*

4. (0, 6), *x*-axis

5. (-3, -7), line *y = x*

Use the following information for problems 6–8. Triangle CDE has the following coordinates: C(4, 0), D(1, 5), and E(8, 8).

6. Which vertex, if any, will remain fixed in place for a reflection over the *x*-axis?

7. Which vertex, if any, will remain fixed in place for a reflection over the line *y = x*?

8. Which vertex, if any, will remain fixed in place for a reflection over the *y*-axis?

For problems 9–10, use the rule (x, y) → (x, -y) and triangle ABC with coordinates A(-1, 4), B(-3, 8), and C(-5, 5).

9. In which quadrant will the image of triangle *ABC* be after the given reflection?

10. Name the coordinates of the image of figure *ABC*.

LESSON (42)
POINT REFLECTION AND POINT SYMMETRY

KEY CONCEPTS YOU'LL NEED IN THIS LESSON

1. When a figure is reflected through a point, every point on the figure has an image. The image point and the original point are equidistant from the **point of reflection**. The point of reflection is the midpoint of a segment connecting an original point to its reflection.

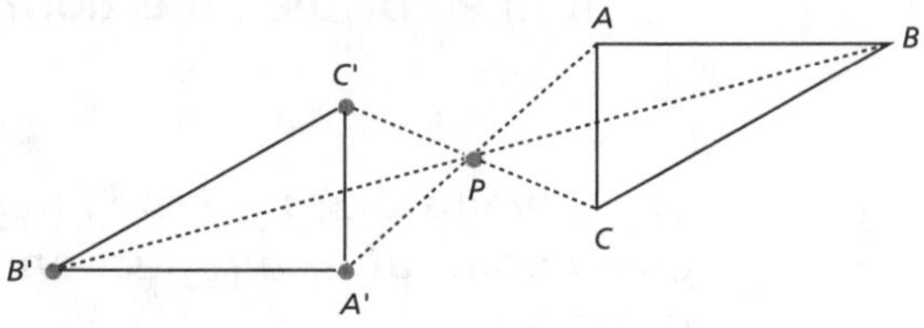

   In the figure, A' is the image of A after a reflection in point P. B' is the reflection of B and C' is the reflection of C. So, AP = PA', BP = PB', and CP = PC'

   In point reflection, a figure and its image are always congruent.

2. On the coordinate plane, the rule for a reflection in the origin, point (0, 0), is:
   $(x, y) \rightarrow (-x, -y)$

3. A figure has point symmetry if, when it is reflected through a point, the result can be given a half-turn and appear unchanged.

---

1   POINT REFLECTION

(EXAMPLE 1)   **In the figure, triangle QPR is the image of triangle NPM after a reflection in point P**
   a. Name the image of each vertex in triangle NPM.
   b. Name all pairs of congruent segments.

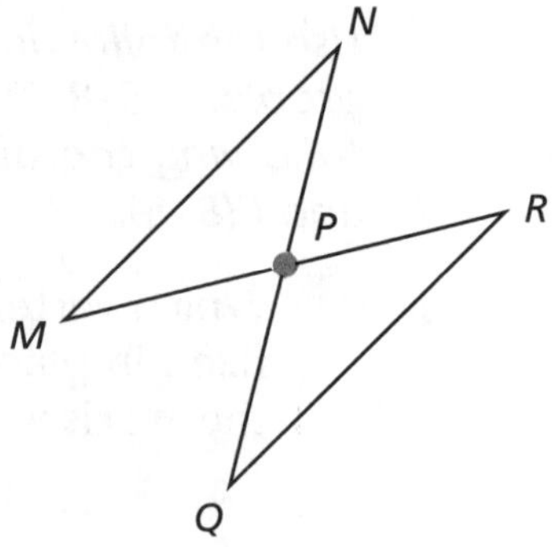

Strategy:	**Use Key Concept 1.**
Step 1:	Name the image of each point in triangle NPM. The image of each point passes through point P. So, $M \rightarrow R$, $N \rightarrow Q$, and $P \rightarrow P$
Step 2:	Name all pairs of congruent segments. Since the reflection point P is the midpoint of each segment, congruent segments are MP and PR, NP and PQ, and MN and QR (since the triangles are congruent).

EXAMPLE 2

Find the image of triangle *ABC* with vertices *A*(1, 5), *B*(4, 4), and *C*(2, 1) after a reflection through the origin.

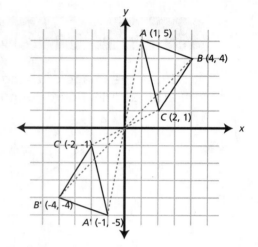

Strategy : Use Key Concept 2.

Step 1: Use the rule $(x, y) \rightarrow (-x, -y)$ for each vertex of the triangle.

$(1, 5) \rightarrow (-1, -5)$, $(4, 4) \rightarrow (-4, -4)$, $(2, 1) \rightarrow (-2$ -$1)$

2 POINT SYMMETRY

EXAMPLE 3

Which of the following letters have point symmetry?

O   T   M   S   Z

Strategy: Use Key Concept 3.

Step 1: In each figure, visualize a point near the center. If a point on one side of the figure is reflected through that central point, the image should be on the figure.

Solution: The letters O, S, and Z have point symmetry.

REGENTS MATH PRACTICE

1. Draw the image of triangle *ABC* after a reflection through point *B*.

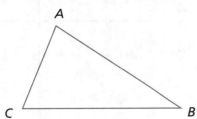

2. In the figure you drew for question 1, name all congruent segments.

In problems 3–6, find the image of the point after a reflection in the origin.

3. (5, -7)

4. (0, 4)

5. (-3, 9)

6. (-2, -6)

7. Draw *WXYZ*, the image of figure *RSTU* after a reflection in the origin if the coordinates of its vertices are *R*(-3, -4), *S*(-1, 0), *T*(-3, 6) and *U*(-5, 2).

8. For the figure in question 7, what is the reflection of segment *RS*?

9. For the figure in question 7, what side is congruent to $\overline{TU}$?

10. Of the following figures, which is the only one that does not have point symmetry?
    a. circle
    b. square
    c. rectangle
    d. equilateral triangle

LESSON 43
TRANSLATIONS, ROTATIONS, AND DILATIONS

KEY CONCEPTS YOU'LL NEED IN THIS LESSON

1. A **translation** is a motion in a plane in which every point moves the same distance in the same direction. In a translation, the original and its image are congruent.

2. On the coordinate plane, the rule for a translation is $(x, y) \rightarrow (x + a, y + b)$ where a is the number of units moved horizontally and b is the number of units moved vertically.

3. A **rotation** is a turn around a point in the plane. Rotations are measured in degrees. As with reflections and translations, in a rotation, the original and its image are congruent.

4. On the coordinate plane, the rule for a rotation of 90° counterclockwise around the origin is $(x, y) \rightarrow (-y, x)$

5. A **dilation** is an enlargement or reduction of a figure from a fixed point. In a dilation, the image is similar to, but not congruent to the original. The **constant of dilation** is the ratio of length of the image to the length of the original.

6. On the coordinate plane, when a figure is to be enlarged by a factor of k, the rule for dilation is $(x, y) \rightarrow (kx, ky)$

---

1 TRANSLATIONS

EXAMPLE 1

M	N	O	P
Q	R	S	T
U	V	W	X

To move M to T by a translation, move 3 units right and 1 unit down.

Describe the translation needed to move W to N.

Strategy: Use Key Concept 1.

Step 1: Describe the horizontal movement first.
Move 1 unit left.

Step 2: Describe the vertical movement.
Move 2 units up.

Solution: To translate W to N, move 1 unit left and 2 units up.

Notice: Photocopying any part of this book is forbidden by law.

EXAMPLE 2

Describe the translation that moved triangle ABC to triangle A'B'C'.

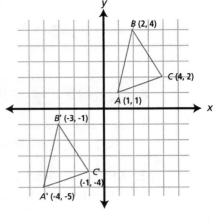

Strategy: **Use Key Concept 2.**

Step 1: Find a, the description of the horizontal, or x-coordinate, move.
Choose any points since all points move the same distance and direction.
Choose points A and A'.
$(1, 1) \rightarrow (-4, -5)$
$1 + a = -4$
$a = -5$

Step 2: Find b, the description of the vertical, or y-coordinate, move.
Again, use points A and A'.
$(1, 1) \rightarrow (-4, -5)$
$1 + b = -5$
$b = -6$

Solution: **The rule that moved triangle ABC to A'B'C' is $(x - 5, y - 6)$.**

---

2 ROTATIONS

EXAMPLE 3

Through how many degrees has point A been rotated around point P?

Strategy: **Use Key Concept 3.**

Step 1: Connect any point on the original figure and the corresponding point on its image to point P to form angle APA'.

Step 2: Measure angle APA'.
$m\angle APA' = 135°$

Solution: **The point has been rotated 135° in a counterclockwise direction.**

EXAMPLE 4

Draw the image of triangle *MNP* after a 90° counterclockwise rotation around the origin.

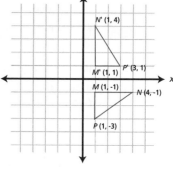

Strategy: Use Key Concept 4.

Step 1: Use the rule for rotations around the origin:
$(x, y) \rightarrow (-y, x)$
$M(1, -1) \rightarrow M'(1, 1)$
$N(4, -1) \rightarrow N'(1, 4)$
$P(1, -3) \rightarrow P'(3, 1)$

Solution: The coordinates are $M'(1, 1)$, $N'(1, 4)$, and $P'(3, 1)$.

---

3 DILATIONS

EXAMPLE 5

In the figure, $\overline{YZ}$ is a dilation of $\overline{WX}$ from point *P*.
a. Find the measure of $\overline{YZ}$.
b. Find the constant of dilation.

Strategy: Use Key Concept 5.

Step 1: Since the triangles are similar, set up a proportion to solve for *YZ*.
$$\frac{WX}{YZ} = \frac{PW}{PY} \rightarrow \frac{2}{YZ} = \frac{3}{7} \rightarrow YZ = \frac{14}{3} = 4\frac{2}{3}$$

Step 2: Find the constant of dilation.

The constant of dilation is the ratio of the image to the original.

$$\frac{YZ}{WX} = \frac{4\frac{2}{3}}{2} = 2\frac{1}{3}$$

Solution: The length of $\overline{YZ}$ is $4\frac{2}{3}$; the constant of dilation is $2\frac{1}{3}$.

EXAMPLE 6

Point (-3, 5) is dilated by the rule $(x, y) \rightarrow (3x, 3y)$.
a. Name the constant of dilation, *k*.
b. Find the image of (-3, 5) under the given dilation.

Strategy: Use Key Concept 6.

Step 1: Use the rule $(x, y) \rightarrow (kx, ky)$ to name the value of *k*.
According to the rule, $k = 3$.

Step 2: Find the image of (-3, 5) using the rule.
$(-3, 5) \rightarrow (3(-3), 3(5)) \rightarrow (-9, 15)$

Solution: The constant of dilation is 3; the image of (-3, 5) is (-9, 15).

REGENTS MATH PRACTICE

1. Under a translation, the image of point (-1, 7) is (4, 9). Find the rule for the translation.

2. What is the image of point (4, -3) after it is translated according to the rule $(x – 6, y + 1)$?

3. The image of point (2, 9) after a translation is (4, 6). What is the image of point (8, 11) after the same translation?

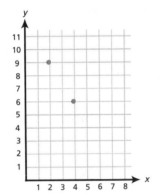

4.

M	N	O	P
Q	R	S	T
U	V	W	X

The image of U after a translation is S. What is the image of R under the same translation?

5. Choose another point on the original ray in Example 3. Find the corresponding point on the rotation image. Connect each point to point P with a line segment. Predict the measure of the angle

formed at P by the two segments. Then measure to test your prediction. How did you predict the measure of the angle?

6.

What is the image of point A after a 135° counterclockwise rotation about point O?

7. How many degrees must point G be rotated counterclockwise around point O so that its image is E?

8. Vertex R of triangle RST has coordinates (-7, 2). What are the coordinates of R' after a 90° counterclockwise rotation about the origin?

9. What is the constant of dilation k if the image of (10, 4) is (5, 2)?

10. Find the image of the point (4, 9) after a dilation if the constant of dilation is 4.

LESSON 44
LOCUS

KEY CONCEPTS YOU'LL NEED IN THIS LESSON

1. A **locus** (plural **loci**) is the set of all points that satisfy a given condition or set of conditions.

2. The five basic loci are:

If there are	_Then the locus is_
• 2 fixed points	The perpendicular bisector of the segment between the points
• 2 intersecting lines	The pair of lines that bisect the angles formed by the pair of lines
• 2 parallel lines	A line parallel to both and halfway between them
• A line and a given distance from the line	Two lines, each parallel to the given line, at the given distance
• A point and a given distance from the point	A circle whose center is at the point and whose radius is the given distance

The 5 basic loci can be used to discover a probable locus.

3. In the coordinate plane, you can write the **equation of the locus** for a set of points that satisfy a given condition.

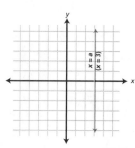

a. The locus of all points whose x-coordinate is a is a line parallel to the y-axis with equation $x = a$.

Notice: Photocopying any part of this book is forbidden by law.

b. The locus of all points whose y-coordinate is b is a line parallel to the x-axis with equation $y = b$.

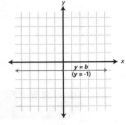

c. The locus of all points that are r units from the origin is a circle with center (0, 0), whose radius is r, and whose equation is $x^2 + y^2 = r^2$.

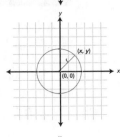

In general, for any fixed point (a, b), the locus of points r units away from the point is $(x - a)^2 + (y - b)^2 = r^2$.

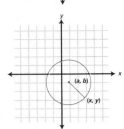

4. If two sets of conditions are given, the locus of points that satisfy both conditions is the intersection of points that satisfy each condition. The locus of all points that are 2 units from the x-axis and all points that are 5 units from the origin is the intersection of the two loci, namely the 4 points shown.

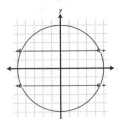

1 **DISCOVERING A PROBABLE LOCUS**

EXAMPLE 1 **What is the locus of points that are equidistant from first base and second base on a baseball diamond?**

Strategy:	**Use Key Concept 2.**
Step 1:	Recognize that the two bases represent two fixed points. Draw a diagram of the two points.
Step 2:	Draw several points that satisfy the condition.
Step 3:	Draw a line through the points.
Solution:	**The locus of points equidistant from first and second base is a straight line that is the perpendicular bisector of the line connecting the bases.**

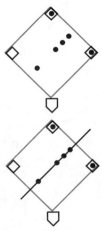

EXAMPLE 2   What is the locus of the midpoints of the radii of a given circle?

Strategy: Use Key Concept 2.

Step 1:   Draw or visualize a circle with many radii drawn.

Step 2:   Draw or visualize the midpoints of these radii connected in order.

Solution: **The locus of the midpoints of the radii of a given circle is a circle whose radius is half the radius of the given circle.**

---

2   EQUATION OF THE LOCUS

EXAMPLE 3   Write the equation of the locus of points that are 7 units from the *y*-axis and to its left.

Strategy: Use Key Concept 3a.

Step 1:   Recognize that a line parallel to the *y*-axis has equation $x = a$.

Step 2:   Write the equation of the line that meets the condition in Step 1: $x = -7$

Solution: **The equation of the locus of points that are 7 units from the *y*-axis and to the left of it is $x = -7$.**

EXAMPLE 4   Write the equation of the locus of points that are parallel to the *x*-axis and pass through the point (2, -5).

Strategy: Use Key Concept 3b.

Step 1:   Recognize that a line parallel to the *x*-axis has equation $y = b$.

Step 2:   Recognize that a line parallel to the *x*-axis passing through the point (2, -5) is 5 units from the *x*-axis and below it.

Step 3:   Write the equation of the line that meets the conditions in Steps 1 and 2: $y = -5$

Solution: **The equation that meets the given conditions is $y = -5$.**

EXAMPLE 5

Write an equation of the locus of points whose distance from the origin is 5.
Decide whether the point (-3, -4) is on the locus.

Strategy: **Use Key Concept 3c.**

Step 1: Write the equation of a circle, the locus of all points a given distance from the origin.
$x^2 + y^2 = r^2$

Step 2: Substitute the length of the radius into the equation.
$x^2 + y^2 = 5^2 \rightarrow x^2 + y^2 = 25$

Step 3: Decide whether (-3, -4) is on the locus (on the circle).
Substitute the values for x and y into the equation of the circle.
$(-3)^2 + (-4)^2 = 25$?
$9 + 16 = 25$?
$25 = 25$ ✔

The values $x = -3$, $y = -4$ make the equation true. Therefore, the point (-3, -4) is on the circle.

Solution: **The equation of the locus of points 5 units from the origin is $x^2 + y^2 = 25$. The point (-3, -4) is on the locus.**

EXAMPLE 6

Find the center and length of the radius of a circle whose equation is $(x - 4)^2 + (y + 1)^2 = 49$.

Strategy: **Same as Example 5.**

Step 1: Use the general equation for any circle with center at (a, b) and radius r.
$(x - a)^2 + (y - b)^2 = r^2$

Step 2: Substitute the known values into the general form:
$(x - 4)^2 + (y - (-1))^2 = 7^2$

Step 3: Write the values from the equation:
$a = 4, b = -1, r = 7$

Solution: **A circle with the given equation has its center at (4, -1) and a radius of 7.**

3 SATISFYING TWO SETS OF CONDITIONS (INTERSECTIONS)

EXAMPLE 7   Draw the locus of points whose equation is $x^2 + y^2 = 4$. Draw the locus of points 1 unit from the x-axis and above it. Find the number of points that satisfy both conditions.

Strategy: **Use Key Concept 4.**

Step 1:   Draw a circle with center at the origin and radius 2.

Step 2:   Draw the line with equation $y = 1$.

Step 3:   Note the points on intersection. There are 2 points.

Solution: **There are two points that satisfy both given conditions.**

REGENTS MATH PRACTICE

1. What is the locus of points that are equidistant from two opposite sides of a rectangle?

2. What is the locus of points that are in a square and equidistant from two consecutive sides of the square?

3. What is the locus of points equidistant from two concentric circles whose radii measure 9 in. and 21 in.? (Concentric circles are circles with the same center.)

4. What is the locus of points that are equidistant from points X and Y?

5. What is the locus of all points in the plane that are 23 mm from point C?

6. What is the locus of points that are 3 in. from line l?

7. Write the equation of the locus of points that are 2 units from the x-axis and below it.

8. Write the equation of the locus of points that are 8 units from the y-axis and to its right.

9. What is the equation of the locus of points that are parallel to the y-axis and pass through the point (-3, -6)?

In problems 10–12, write the equation of the locus of points whose distance from the origin is given.

10. 10

11. 1

12. $\sqrt{18}$

In problems 13–17, find the center and the length of the radius for a circle with the given equation.

13. $(x - 2)^2 + (y - 3)^2 = 81$

14. $(x + 2)^2 + (y)^2 = 14$

15. $(x + 8)^2 + (y - 2)^2 = 121$

16. $(x + 9)^2 + (y + 3)^2 = 10$

17. $(x - 1)^2 + (y - 1)^2 = 3$

18. Write the following loci: the equation of the locus of points 3 units from the origin and the equation of the locus of points parallel to the x-axis that pass through the point (0, 3). How many points satisfy both conditions?

19. Describe the locus of points that are equidistant from the points (4, 0) and (0, 4).

20. Write the equation of the locus of points 6 units from the point (3, 5). Write the equation of the locus of points parallel to the y-axis and 7 units to the right. How many points satisfy both conditions?

UNIT 8 REVIEW

1. Triangle *ABC* has coordinates *A*(-2, 3), *B*(3, 4), and *C*(2, -1). Find the area of the triangle.

2. In the word CHANGE, which letters have line symmetry?

3. What is the image of the point whose coordinates are (-6, 7) after a reflection in the x-axis?

4. If the image of a point after a reflection in the line $y = x$ is (4, -9), what were the coordinates of the original point?

5. Which letters in the word HOTEL have point symmetry?

6. What are the coordinates of the point whose image is (8, -3) after a reflection in the origin?

7. What is the rule for a translation if the point (12, -2) is the image of the point (15, 4)?

8. Describe the image of the letter *H* after a 180° counterclockwise rotation about the center of the horizontal line of the letter.

9. What is the locus of all points in rhombus *ABCD* that are equidistant from vertices *A* and *C*?

10. What is the equation of the locus of points whose distance from the origin is 20?

LESSON ⁴⁵
DISPLAYING DATA IN TABLES AND HISTOGRAMS

KEY CONCEPTS YOU'LL NEED IN THIS LESSON

1. A **frequency table** (or interval table) must have intervals of equal size.

2. The intervals must account for all the data. Both the greatest and least values must be included in the table.

3. The intervals must not overlap, so that each score can be placed in only one interval.

4. A reasonable number of intervals, from approximately 5 to approximately 10, allows data to be grouped so that patterns can be seen.

5. A **frequency histogram** is a bar graph in which data from a frequency table are displayed. The bars are drawn next to one another to indicate that as one interval ends, the next begins.

---

❶ FREQUENCY TABLES

EXAMPLE 1

The data below give the amounts of money in dollars that 32 students estimate they spend during an average week.
10, 17, 20, 15, 22, 30, 25, 10,
20, 15, 24, 18, 21, 22, 25, 12,
13, 18, 20, 20, 14, 17, 25, 30,
6, 10, 16, 20, 14, 19, 28, 22

a. Complete a frequency table.
b. How many students estimate that they spend more than $20 per week?
c. In which interval does the greatest number of students fall?

Strategy: **Use Key Concepts 1– 4.**

Step 1: Choose an appropriate interval for the data.
An interval of $10 would give just 3 intervals: $1–$10, $11–$20, and $21–$30, not enough to get a good sense of the data.
An interval of $5 would give 6 intervals, a better number for the data.

Step 2: Copy and complete a frequency table, using tallies.

Interval	Tallies	Frequency (Number)
1–5		0
6–10	||||	4
11–15	‖‖‖ |	6
16–20	‖‖‖ ‖‖‖ |	11
21–25	‖‖‖ |||	8
26–30	|||	3

Step 3: Use the data in the table to find the number of students who estimate that they spend more than $20 per week.
The last two rows represent those students.
8 + 3 = 11, so 11 students estimate that they spend more than $20.

Step 4: Read the table to find the interval in which the greatest number of students fall.
The interval $16–$20 contains the greatest number of students.

② FREQUENCY HISTOGRAMS

EXAMPLE 2 **Display the data from Example 1 in a frequency histogram.**

Strategy: **Use Key Concept 5.**

Step 1: Give titles and values to the axes. The horizontal axis represents the amounts of money (the intervals), each interval representing $5. The vertical axis represents the number of students (the frequencies), each line representing 1 student.

Step 2: Draw the bars. Note that only the first interval, $1–$5 has no bar. This is so because no students estimated within that range. All other bars are touching.

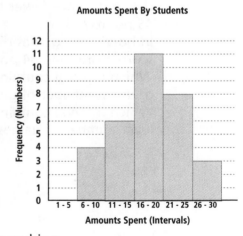

REGENTS MATH PRACTICE

1. The data below represent the number of points a high school basketball team scored during one season.

    45, 43, 64, 49, 47, 55, 51, 54, 44, 41, 62, 50, 49, 61, 42, 47, 40, 53, 45, 60, 48, 56, 61, 60, 43

    a. Copy and complete the frequency table.

Interval	Tallies	Frequency (Number)
40 – 44		
45 – 49		
50 – 54		
55 – 59		
60 – 64		

    Answer the following questions from the frequency table.

    b. In how many games did the team score fewer than 45 points?
    c. In how many games did they score more than 54 points?
    d. Which interval contains the greatest number of games?
    e. Which interval contains the least number of games?

2. What is the total frequency (the total number of games) shown in the table?

3. In constructing a frequency histogram of the data, what will the horizontal axis represent?

4. What will the vertical axis represent?

5. In the space below, construct a frequency histogram for the data.

LESSON 46
MEASURES OF CENTRAL TENDENCY

KEY CONCEPTS YOU'LL NEED IN THIS LESSON

1. The **mean** is the average when the total of the scores is divided by the number of scores.

2. The **median** is the middle score when the scores are arranged numerically from least to greatest.

3. The **mode** is the score or scores that occur the greatest number of times. A set of data may have no mode.

4. Mean, median, and mode can be found for data in a frequency table.
    a. If the interval in the table is one number, all three measures can be found.
    b. If the interval in the table is greater than one number (a range of numbers), you can find the interval containing the mode and the median.

1 THE MEAN

EXAMPLE 1

Kim made telephone calls of the following number of minutes to a friend in New Jersey: 5, 8, 12, 16, 7, 10, and 8. What was the mean number of minutes her calls lasted, rounded to the nearest minute?

Strategy: **Use Key Concept 1.**

Step 1: Add to find the sum of the scores (minutes).
$5 + 8 + 12 + 16 + 7 + 10 + 8 = 66$

Step 2: Divide the sum by the number of scores (telephone calls).
$66 \div 7 \approx 9.43$

Solution: **Rounded to the nearest minute, Kim's calls lasted an average of 9 minutes.**

EXAMPLE 2

Andrew's average on 4 tests is exactly 90. He received a grade of 90 on one test, 82 on another, and the same grade on each of the other two tests. What grade did he receive on each of the other two tests?

Strategy: Use Key Concept 1 and an algebraic procedure.

Step 1: Assign a variable to the unknown test score.
Let x = the score Andrew received on each of two tests.

Step 2: Set up and solve and equation that describes the data in the problem.

$$\frac{90 + 82 + \text{the same score on two tests}}{4} = 90$$

$$\frac{90 + 82 + 2 \cdot x}{4} = 90$$

$$\frac{172 + 2x}{4} = 90$$

$$172 + 2x = 360$$
$$2x = 188$$
$$x = 94$$

Solution: Andrew received a score of 94 on each of his other two tests.

---

② THE MEDIAN

EXAMPLE 3

The prices of six CDs rounded to the nearest dollar are:
$12, $15, $14, $17, $12, and $11.
What is the median price paid for the CDs?

Strategy: Use Key Concept 2.

Step 1: Arrange the scores (prices) in order from least to greatest.
$11, $12, $12, $14, $15, $17
Since there are 6 scores, an even number, there is no middle score.

Step 2: Find the average or mean of the two middle scores.
$11, $12, **$12, $14**, $15, $17

$$\frac{\$12 + \$14}{2} = \frac{\$26}{2} = \$13$$

Solution: The median price paid for the six CDs is $13.

3 THE MODE

EXAMPLE 4 For the CDs described in Example 3, what is the mode price paid?

Strategy: Use Key Concept 3.

Step 1: Examine the data for the most frequently occurring score (price). $12 occurs more often than any other price.

Solution: The mode price paid for the CDs is $12.

4 DATA IN A FREQUENCY TABLE AND MEASURES OF CENTRAL TENDENCY

EXAMPLE 5 The data in the table gives the number of blocks from school 15 students live.

Interval (Number of Blocks)	Frequency (Number of Students)
1	2
2	1
3	0
4	3
5	4
6	2
7	3

Find the mean, median, and mode distances.

Strategy: Use Key Concept 4a, noting that in the table each interval represents a single number.

Find the mean number of blocks students live from school.

Step 1: In each row, multiply the interval (number of blocks) by the frequency (number of students) to find how many blocks are walked in all by students in that row.

Step 2: Add the totals in the last column to find the total number of blocks walked by all students.

Step 3: Divide that total by 15, the number of students.

Interval (blocks)	Frequency (Students)	Interval · Frequency
1	2	1 · 2 = 2
2	1	2 · 1 = 2
3	0	3 · 0 = 0
4	3	4 · 3 = 12
5	4	5 · 4 = 20
6	2	6 · 2 = 12
7	3	7 · 3 = 21

Total Frequency = Total Blocks for 15 students = 69

69 ÷ 15 = 4.6

Solution: **The average number of blocks walked by the 15 students is 4.6.**

Find the median number of blocks.

Interval (Blocks)	Frequency (Students)
1	2
2	1
3	0
4	3
5	**4**
6	2
7	3

Step 1: Find the total frequency: the total frequency is 15.

Step 2: Use the total frequency, 15 to determine which score is the median. The median score is the middle when the scores are in numerical order. Since the scores are in numerical order in the table, the middle score is the 8th score.

Step 3: Find the interval that contains the 8th score.
Count from the top: 2 + 1 + 0 + 3 = 6, but 2 + 1 + 0 + 3 + 4 = 10, which is past the 8th score. So, the 8th score must be in the interval of 5 blocks.

Solution: **The median number of blocks walked is 5.**

Find the mode number of blocks.

Step 1: Find the interval that contains the greatest frequency.
The interval with the greatest frequency is 5, the mode interval.

Solution: **The mode number of blocks walked is 5.**

EXAMPLE 6

The data in the table represent the numbers of minutes of math homework done one night by students in a class.

Interval (Number of Minutes)	Frequency (Number of Students)
10–19	3
20–29	5
30–39	8
40–49	6
50–59	7

Find the modal interval and the interval with the median.

Strategy: **Use Key Concept 4b, noting that each interval is not a single number, but a range.**

Step 1: Find the modal interval.
Find the interval with the greatest frequency. Since more students said they did from 30 to 39 minutes of math homework, the modal interval is 30–39.

Step 2: Find the interval with the median.
Since there are 29 students, the median interval is the interval with the 15th student (14 students above and 14 students below).
Count the frequencies from the top of the table: 3 + 5 = 8, but 3 + 5 + 8 = 16, which is past the 15th score. So the median must be somewhere in the interval 30–39.

Solution: **For the grouped data shown in the table, the modal interval and the interval with the median are both 30–39.**

Note that if the intervals are a range, it is impossible to tell which actual score is the mode or median. For example, every student in the range 30–39 may have done 31 minutes of homework, or the numbers may be spread throughout the range.

REGENTS MATH PRACTICE

1. Steven scored the following on his first four tests: 78, 84, 88, and 82. What is the least grade he must receive on his next test to have an average of 85 for the five tests? Explain how you solved the problem.

2. The average age of four cousins is 42. If one cousin is 32, one is 44, and the other two are twins, how old are the twins?

3. Which statement is true about the following set of data?
18, 17, 21, 24, 21

   a. The mean is greater than the median.
   b. The median is less than the mode.
   c. The mean and median are the same number.
   d. The median and mode are the same number.

4. What must be the next score for the mean, median, and mode of the set of data to all be the same number?
44, 52, 60, 60, ___

Use the data in the table below to answer questions 5–8 about books sold during one hour.

Interval (Books bought)	Frequency (Customers)
0	12
1	3
2	7
3	4
4	2
5	0
6	1

5. How many customers were in the store during the hour?

6. How many customers bought books?

7. What was the mode number of books bought during the hour?

8. To the nearest tenth. what was the mean number bought by all the customers who were in the store during the hour?

Use the data in the table below to answer questions 9–13 about the number of miles per gallon owners said their cars got per gallon of gasoline.

Interval (Miles per gallon)	Frequency (Cars)
15–20	3
21–25	5
26–30	3
31–35	7
36–40	2

9. How many cars are represented in the table?

10. How many car owners said their cars got more than 25 miles per gallon?

11. In which interval is the median?

12. Which is the modal interval?

13. What percent of the owners said their cars got no more than 20 miles per gallon?

LESSON 47
CUMULATIVE FREQUENCY HISTOGRAMS, QUARTILES, PERCENTILES

KEY CONCEPTS YOU'LL NEED IN THIS LESSON

1. To construct a **cumulative frequency table**, add the frequency (number) from each interval to the frequencies for lower intervals.

2. A **cumulative frequency histogram** is drawn using the data from a cumulative frequency table.

3. The cumulative frequency (vertical) scale can be divided into percents. The total frequency represents 100% and 0 on the scale represents 0%.

4. The point on the cumulative frequency scale that represents 25% is the **lower quartile**; 25% of the scores are at or below that score.
   The point that represents 50% is the **second quartile** or the **median**; 50% of the scores are at or below that score.
   The point that represents 75% is the **upper quartile**; 75% of the scores are at or below that score.

5. **Percentiles** break the cumulative frequency scale into 100 equal parts. A percentile tells what percent of scores are at or below a particular score.
   The lower quartile is the 25th percentile.
   The median is the 50th percentile.
   The upper quartile is the 75th percentile.

---

1 CUMULATIVE FREQUENCY TABLES AND CUMULATIVE FREQUENCY HISTOGRAMS

EXAMPLE 1 The frequency table shows the number of students scoring within different intervals on a mathematics test. A frequency histogram for the data in the table is shown.

Interval (Test scores)	Frequency (Number of Students)
91–100	20
81–90	30
71–80	10
61–70	15
51–60	5

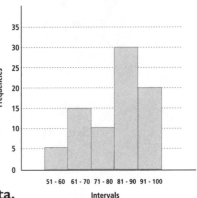

Construct a cumulative frequency table and cumulative frequency histogram from the data.

Strategy: **Use Key Concepts 1 and 2.**

Step 1: Construct a cumulative frequency table. Use the table to construct a cumulative frequency histogram.

Interval (Test Scores)	Frequency (Number of students)	Cumulative Frequency
91–100	20	80 (5+15+10+30+20)
81–90	30	60 (5+15+10+30)
71–80	10	30 (5+15+10)
61–70	15	20 (5 + 15)
51–60	5	5

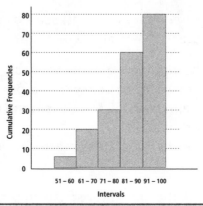

2 QUARTILES AND PERCENTILES

EXAMPLE 2

Find the lower quartile, second quartile (or median), and upper quartile for the data in Example 1.

Strategy: **Use Key Concepts 3 and 4.**

Step 1: Find the lower quartile.
On the cumulative frequency histogram, 25% of 80 students, or 20 students, scored 70 or less. So, 70 is the lower quartile.

Step 2: Find the second quartile or median.
On the cumulative frequency histogram, 50% of 80 students, or 40 students, scored at or below some number in the interval 81–90. So, the second quartile or median is somewhere in the interval 81–90.

Step 3: Find the upper quartile.
On the cumulative frequency histogram, 75% of 80 students, or 60 students, scored 90 or less. So, 90 is the upper quartile.

Notice: Photocopying any part of this book is forbidden by law.

For the data in Example 1, find the score that represents the 30th percentile.

Strategy:	**Use Key Concept 5.**
Step 1:	On the vertical scale, estimate the location of the 30th percentile: it is $\frac{1}{5}$ of the way up from 25% to 50%.
Step 2:	Follow the 30th percentile across to the cumulative frequency histogram. Note that the 30th percentile is somewhere in the range 71–80. The actual score cannot be determined beyond that from the graph.
Solution:	**The 30th percentile is a score somewhere between 71 and 80.**

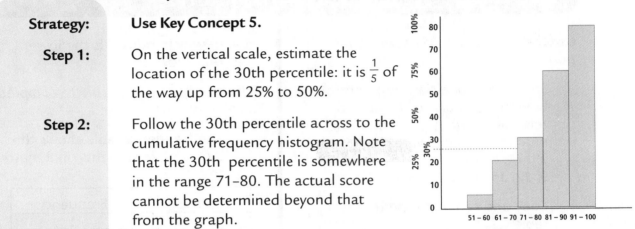

Notice: Photocopying any part of this book is forbidden by law.

203

REGENTS MATH PRACTICE

Use the data below to answer questions 1–5.

Students in one class kept logs of how many hours they watched television during one week. The number of hours were: 10, 15, 13, 25, 21, 7, 18, 12, 15, 16, 20, 20, 18, 9, 12, 15, 23, 24, 5, 8, 4.

1. Copy and complete the frequency table

Interval (Hours)	Frequency (Number of Students)
21–25	
16–20	
11–15	
6–10	
1–5	

2. Copy and complete the cumulative frequency table.

Interval (Hours)	Cumulative Frequency
21–25	
16–20	
11–15	
6–10	
1–5	

3. Construct a cumulative frequency histogram using the data in the above table.

4. In which interval is the median number of hours of television watching?

5. In which interval is the lower quartile?

Use the data in the table to complete problems 6–10.

The frequency table shows the scores of 24 students on a math test.

Interval	Frequency
51–60	1
61–70	9
71–80	4
81–90	6
91–100	4

6. Copy and complete the cumulative frequency table.

Interval	Cumulative Frequency
91–100	
81–90	
71–80	
61–70	
51–60	

7. Construct a cumulative frequency histogram from the cumulative frequency table.

8. In which interval is the median?

9. In which interval is the upper quartile?

10. Approximately what percent of the scores are 70 or less?

LESSON 48
PROBABILITY

KEY CONCEPTS YOU'LL NEED IN THIS LESSON

1. The **sample space** for an experiment is a list of all possible outcomes.
    An **event** is a list of favorable outcomes.
    For the experiment "spin a spinner labeled 1–6 once":

    - The sample space is 1, 2, 3, 4, 5, and 6.

    - Events might be "land on a number greater than 4",
        "land on an odd number",
        "land on a prime number", and so on.

2. The **probability of an event,** written $P(E)$, is the ratio

    $$\frac{\text{Number of favorable outcomes}}{\text{Total number of possible outcomes}}$$

    For the experiment "spin a spinner labeled 1–6 once", the probability of the event "land on a number that is a multiple of 3" is

    $P(E) = \frac{2}{6} = \frac{1}{3}$ since there are 6 possible outcomes and 2 favorable outcomes (3 and 6).

3. The probability of an event that is **impossible** is 0.
    The probability of an event that is **certain** to occur is 1.
    The probability of all events that are neither impossible nor certain is between 0 and 1.

4. The **sum of the probabilities** in a given experiment is always 1.
    For a single toss of a 6-sided die:

    $P(1) = \frac{1}{6}$, $P(2) = \frac{1}{6}$, $P(3) = \frac{1}{6}$, $P(4) = \frac{1}{6}$, $P(5) = \frac{1}{6}$, $P(6) = \frac{1}{6}$, and

    $\frac{1}{6} + \frac{1}{6} + \frac{1}{6} + \frac{1}{6} + \frac{1}{6} + \frac{1}{6} = 1$

    If the probability of an event is $\frac{1}{3}$, then the probability of the event *not* occurring is $1 - \frac{1}{3}$ or $\frac{2}{3}$.

    In general, since $P(\text{event } A) + P(\text{not event } A) = 1$, $P(\text{not } A) = 1 - P(A)$.

5. The **Counting Principle** can be used to solve many probability problems. It is stated as follows: If an event can happen in m ways, followed by an event that can happen in n ways, the total number of ways the two events can happen is $m \times n$.

The Counting Principle can be applied to probabilities as follows: If the probability of an event is *a* and the probability of another independent event is *b*, then the probability of both events occurring is $a \times b$.

Tree diagrams, like the Counting Principle, can be used to represent the outcomes of probability problems.

---

1   **BASIC PROBABILITY**

EXAMPLE 1

For one spin of a spinner labeled 1–8 with 8 equal sections:
a. **What is the sample space?**
b. **What is the probability of the event "land on a number less than 4"?**
c. **What is the probability of the event "land on a number less than 9"?**
d. **What is the probability of the event "land on a number greater than 8"?**
e. **What is the sum of all probabilities for the experiment?**
f. **What is the probability that the spinner will *not* land on a number less than 4?**

Strategy: **Use Key Concepts 1– 4.**

Step 1: Write the sample space: the list of all possible outcomes.
The spinner may land on 1, 2, 3, 4, 5, 6, 7, or 8.
So, the sample space is 1, 2, 3, 4, 5, 6, 7, or 8.

Step 2: Find P(a number less than 4).

Use the ratio: $P(E) = \dfrac{\text{Number of favorable outcomes}}{\text{Total number of possible outcomes}}$

Favorable outcomes are: 1, 2, or 3.
Total number of outcomes = 8
So, P(a number less than 4) = $\dfrac{3}{8}$.

Step 3: Find P(a number less than 9).
Favorable outcomes are 1, 2, 3, 4, 5, 6, 7, and 8.

So, P(a number less than 9) = $\dfrac{8}{8}$ = 1.

The outcome is certain.

Step 4: Find P(a number greater than 8).
There are no favorable outcomes.

So, P(a number greater than 8) = $\frac{0}{8}$ = 0.

The outcome is impossible.

Step 5: The sum of all probabilities is $\frac{1}{8} + \frac{1}{8} + \frac{1}{8} + \frac{1}{8} + \frac{1}{8} + \frac{1}{8} + \frac{1}{8} + \frac{1}{8}$ = 1.

Step 6: Find P(a number not less than 4).

Since P(a number less than 4) = $\frac{3}{8}$,
P(a number not less than 4) = $1 - \frac{3}{8} = \frac{5}{8}$.

So, the probability that the spinner will not land on a number less than 4 is $\frac{5}{8}$.

EXAMPLE 2

Your school cafeteria serves 4 different main courses, 3 different drinks, and 2 different desserts. If a lunch consists of a main course, a drink, and dessert, how many different lunches are possible?

Strategy: **Use Key Concept 5.**

Step 1: Use the Counting Principle to find the total number of lunches.
4 choices × 3 choices × 2 choices = 24
So, there are 24 different possible lunches.

OR

Step 2: Use a tree diagram to model the problem. Use any 4 main courses, 3 drinks, and 2 desserts.
Whichever method you use, there are 24 different possible lunches.

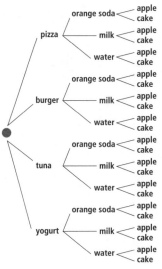

EXAMPLE 3

Suppose the lunches in Example 2 are handed out at random. What is the probability that you will be given your favorite lunch: pizza, orange soda, and an apple?

Strategy: **Use Key Concept 5.**

Step 1: Use the Counting Principle for probabilities.

$P(\text{pizza}) = \frac{1}{4}$, $P(\text{orange soda}) = \frac{1}{3}$, $P(\text{apple}) = \frac{1}{2}$

So, $P(\text{pizza, orange soda, apple}) = \frac{1}{4} \times \frac{1}{3} \times \frac{1}{2} = \frac{1}{24}$

OR

Step 2:   Use a tree diagram to model the problem.
From Example 2, you see that there are 24 different lunches. If they are handed out at random, the probability of getting a particular one is $\frac{1}{24}$.

REGENTS MATH PRACTICE

For each experiment described below, write whether the outcome described is impossible, certain, or uncertain.

1. Getting a number less than 7 on one roll of a die.

2. Picking a blue marble from a bag containing 1 blue, 20 red, and 50 green.

3. Spinning a vowel on a 5-section spinner labeled B, C, D, G, H.

4. Opening your math book to two facing pages whose page numbers add to an even number.

5. Picking two cards whose sum is even from a bag with cards numbered 1–50.

6. From the same bag, picking two cards whose sum is less than 100.

Use the spinner below to answer questions 7–13.

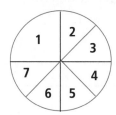

On one spin of the spinner, what is the probability that the spinner will land on

7. 2?
   a. $\frac{1}{7}$ b. $\frac{1}{8}$ c. $\frac{2}{7}$ d. $\frac{2}{8}$

8. an even number?
   a. $\frac{3}{8}$ b. $\frac{3}{7}$ c. $\frac{2}{7}$ d. $\frac{6}{8}$

9. 1?
   a. $\frac{1}{8}$ b. $\frac{1}{7}$ c. $\frac{1}{4}$ d. $\frac{3}{4}$

10. any number other than 1?
    a. $\frac{1}{8}$ b. $\frac{6}{7}$ c. $\frac{7}{8}$ d. $\frac{3}{4}$

11. a prime number?
    a. $\frac{1}{2}$ b. $\frac{3}{8}$ c. $\frac{3}{7}$ d. $\frac{1}{4}$

12. a multiple of 8?
    a. 1   b. $\frac{7}{8}$ c. $\frac{1}{8}$ d. 0

13. a factor of 8?
    a. $\frac{1}{4}$ b. $\frac{3}{8}$ c. $\frac{3}{7}$ d. $\frac{1}{2}$

14. You have 7 pairs of shorts, 10 T-shirts, and 2 pairs of sneakers. How many different outfits can you make consisting of shorts, T-shirt, and sneakers?

In questions 15–18, assume that you select an outfit randomly. In each case find the probability of selecting the outfit described.

15. any outfit that includes your blue shorts.

16. any outfit that includes your red shorts and black sneakers.

17. any outfit that includes your blue shorts and your black T-shirt.

18. your one favorite outfit.

Use the following information to answer questions 19–20. There are 5 airlines that fly between New York City and Chicago. There are 4 airlines that fly between Chicago and San Francisco.

19. How many different ways can you fly from New York City to San Francisco going through Chicago?

20. If you choose at random, what is the probability that you will fly American from New York City to Chicago and Northwest from Chicago to San Francisco?

LESSON ⁴⁹
MORE PROBABILITY

KEY CONCEPTS YOU'LL NEED IN THIS LESSON

1. $P(A \text{ and } B)$ is found by finding the probability of all outcomes that are in **both** event A **and** event B.

2. $P(A \text{ or } B)$ is found by finding the probability of all outcomes that are in **either** event A **or** event B **or in both events**.

   $P(A \text{ or } B) = P(A) + P(B) - P(A \text{ and } B)$

3. The probability of any **compound event** can be found by

   - Drawing a tree diagram to represent the sample space, then
   - Counting the total number of outcomes in the sample space, then
   - Counting the number of favorable outcomes, and finally
   - Writing the probability as the fraction $\dfrac{\text{number of favorable outcomes}}{\text{total number of outcomes}}$.

4. A compound probability problem may involve **replacement** or **no replacement**. When you toss a die several times, the probability of getting a particular number is a problem with replacement. The die is always the same. When you eat candies from a bag, the probability of choosing specific candies is a problem without replacement because the contents of the bag changes (gets smaller) each time you choose.

① PROBABILITY OF A AND B

EXAMPLE 1

A spinner with 8 equal sections numbered 1–8 is spun once. What is the probability that it lands on a number that is even and less than 7?

Strategy: **Use Key Concept 1.**

Step 1: List all the outcomes that are even: 2, 4, 6, 8.
List all the outcomes that are less than 7: 1, 2, 3, 4, 5, 6

Step 2: Find the outcomes that are on both lists: 2, 4, 6 (three outcomes)

Step 3: Write the probability as a fraction.

$P(\text{even and less than 7}) = \dfrac{3}{8}$

Solution: **On one spin, the probability of getting an even number and a number less than 7 is $\dfrac{3}{8}$.**

2   PROBABILITY OF *A* OR *B*

EXAMPLE 2

For the spinner described in Example 1, what is the probability that on one spin, the outcome will be either a number less than 4 or an odd number?

Strategy: **Use Key Concept 2.**

Step 1:   Find the probability of *A*, getting a number less than 4.

There are 3 numbers less than 4: 1, 2, and 3.

So, $P(\text{less than 4}) = \frac{3}{8}$.

Step 2:   Find the probability of *B*, getting an odd number.
There are 4 odd numbers: 1, 3, 5, and 7. So, $P(\text{odd}) = \frac{4}{8}$.

Step 3:   Find the probability of *A* and *B*, getting a number less than 4 that is odd.

There are 2 numbers less than 4 that are odd: 1 and 3.

So, $P(\text{less than 4 and odd}) = \frac{2}{8}$.

Step 4:   Find the probability of getting a number less than 4 or an odd number.

$$P(A \text{ or } B) = P(A) + P(B) - P(A \text{ and } B)$$
$$P(\text{less than 4 or odd}) = P(\text{less than 4}) + P(\text{odd}) - P(\text{less than 4 and odd})$$
$$= \frac{3}{8} + \frac{4}{8} - \frac{2}{8}$$
$$= \frac{7}{8} - \frac{2}{8}$$
$$= \frac{5}{8}$$

Solution: **The probability of getting a number less than 4 or odd is $\frac{5}{8}$.**

EXAMPLE 3

For the spinner in Example 1, find the probability of getting an even number or a 5.

Strategy: **Use Key Concept 2 again.**

Step 1:   Find the probability of each event.

$P(\text{even number}) = \frac{4}{8}; \; P(5) = \frac{1}{8}$

Step 2:   Use the rule:

$$P(A \text{ or } B) = P(A) + P(B) - P(A \text{ and } B)$$
$$P(\text{even or 5}) = P(\text{even}) + P(5) - P(\text{even and 5})$$

$= \frac{4}{8} + \frac{1}{8} - 0$ (There are no numbers both even and 5)

$= \frac{5}{8}$

Solution: The probability of getting an even number or a 5 is $\frac{5}{8}$.

---

3 **COMPOUND EVENTS AND TREE DIAGRAMS**

EXAMPLE 4 **If 3 coins are tossed simultaneously, find the probability of getting at least 2 heads.**

Strategy: **Use Key Concept 3.**

Step 1: Draw a tree diagram representing all possible outcomes.

H — H — H (H, H, H)
H — T (H, H, T)
H — T — H (H, T, H)
T (H, T, T)
T — H — H (T, H, H)
T (T, H, T)
T — T — H (T, T, H)
T (T, T, T)

Step 2: Count along each branch to find the total number of outcomes.
There are 8 possible outcomes.

Step 3: Count the number of outcomes that meet the condition: at least 2 heads.
There are 4 outcomes that contain at least 2 heads (either 2 heads or 3 heads).

Solution: **The probability of getting at least 2 heads is $\frac{4}{8}$ or $\frac{1}{2}$.**

---

4 **PROBABILITY WITH AND WITHOUT REPLACEMENT**

EXAMPLE 5 **What is the probability of getting 3 consecutive 4's on three spins of the spinner in Example 1?**

Strategy: **Use Key Concept 4, Probability With Replacement.**

Step 1: Find the probability at each stage.

$$P(4) = \frac{1}{8}$$

$$P(4) = \frac{1}{8}$$

$$P(4) = \frac{1}{8}$$

Step 2: Use the Counting Principle.

$$P(4, \text{ then } 4, \text{ then } 4) = \frac{1}{8} \times \frac{1}{8} \times \frac{1}{8} = \frac{1}{512}$$

Solution: **The probability of getting consecutive 4s on three spins is $\frac{1}{512}$.**

EXAMPLE 6

Two cards are drawn from a standard deck of 52 playing cards. If the first card is not replaced in the deck after being drawn, what is the probability that both are queens?

Strategy: **Use Key Concept 4, Probability Without Replacement.**

Step 1: Find the probability that the first card is a queen.

There are 4 queens, so the $P(\text{queen}) = \frac{4}{52}$ or $\frac{1}{13}$.

Step 2: Find the probability that the second card is a queen.
If the first card drawn was a queen, there are 3 queens left in the deck.
There are also only 51 cards left since the first card was not replaced.

So, for the second draw, $P(\text{queen}) = \frac{3}{51}$ or $\frac{1}{17}$.

Step 3: Use the Counting Principle.

$$P(\text{two queens}) = \frac{1}{13} \times \frac{1}{17} = \frac{1}{221}$$

Solution: **The probability of drawing two queens if the first card is not replaced is $\frac{1}{221}$.**

REGENTS MATH PRACTICE

1. A fair die and a coin are tossed together. Find the probability of getting
   a. a 5 and heads.
   b. an odd number and tails.
   c. a prime number and heads.
   d. a number greater than 4 and tails.
   e. a number greater than 6 and heads.
   f. a number less than 9 and tails.

2. A spinner with 6 equal sections numbered 1–6 is spun once. What is the probability of getting
   a. an even number greater than 3?
   b. an odd number less than 5?
   c. a prime number less than 3?
   d. a 3 or a 6?
   e. an odd number that is not prime?
   f. an even number that is not prime?

3. A single candy is randomly picked from a bag containing 4 red candies, 5 green candies, and 1 blue candy. Find the probability that the candy picked is
   a. blue
   b. either red or green
   c. not green
   d. neither green nor blue
   e. either green or blue
   f. white

4. One card is drawn from a standard deck of 52 playing cards. Find the probability that it is
   a. a three or a seven
   b. a picture card
   c. a 9 or a heart
   d. either a heart or a diamond
   e. not an ace
   f. neither an ace nor a queen

5. If you guess on all 5 questions of a true-false test, what is the probability that you will get all 5 correct?

6. If you meet a family with three children, what is the probability that there are exactly 2 girls?

7. If you toss 3 coins, what is the probability of getting
   a. no heads
   b. all heads
   c. exactly one heads
   d. exactly two tails
   e. no tails

8. Explain the relationship between the answers to questions 7b and 7e above.

9. A bag contains 2 red cubes, 3 blue cubes, and 5 green cubes. A cube is removed, examined, and re-placed in the bag. If a second cube is drawn, what is the probability that
   a. both cubes are red?
   b. the first is red and the second is blue?
   c. the first is red and the second is green?
   d. both are green?
   e. neither is blue?

10. A card is drawn from a standard deck and not replaced. A second card is then drawn. What is the probability that
    a. both cards are red?
    b. both cards are aces?
    c. both cards are hearts?
    d. the first card is an ace and the second card is a 5?
    e. the first card is a spade and the second card is a diamond?

LESSON 50
PERMUTATIONS

KEY CONCEPTS YOU'LL NEED IN THIS LESSON

1. A **permutation** is an arrangement of a set of objects in a particular order. Each different order is a different arrangement.

   - The possible arrangements of the letters A, E, and T are AET, ATE, EAT, ETA, TAE, and TEA. For the 3 letters, there are 6 permutations.

2. **Factorials** can be used to solve permutation problems.

   - In how many ways can 5 students be assigned to do 5 problems on the chalkboard if each student does one problem?

   Use the Counting Principle to solve the problem.

First problem		**Second**		**Third**		**Fourth**		**Fifth**	
5 students	$\times$	4	$\times$	3	$\times$	2	$\times$	1	= 120 different ways.

   In factorial notation, 5! means $5 \times 4 \times 3 \times 2 \times 1$, or 120.

   In general, the number of possible permutations for n things taken n at a time is found by the formula $_nP_n = n!$

   - In how many ways can 4 different books be arranged on a shelf?

   Since all 4 books are being used, the value of $_nP_n$ gives the answer.
   When $n = 4$, $_nP_n = 4! = 4 \times 3 \times 2 \times 1 = 24$ ways.
   Your calculator has a factorial key.

3. Where the number of items taken at a time is less than the total number of items, the number of possible permutations is found by the formula: $_nP_r = \dfrac{n!}{(n-r)!}$ where n is the total number of items and r is the number being used at a time.

   - How many different 3-letter "words" can be formed from the letters of the word TODAY?

   Since only 3 out of 5 letters will be used, the value of $_nP_r$ gives the answer where $n = 5$ and $r = 3$.
   $$_5P_3 = \frac{5!}{(5-3)!} = \frac{120}{2} = 60 \text{ different "words"}$$

4. The number of permutations of n items taken n at a time is reduced if several of the items are identical. The formula for the number of permutations of n items taken n at a time if r items are identical is $\dfrac{n!}{r!}$

   - How many different 6-letter "words" are possible using the letters of the word APPLES?

   Since the letter P is used twice, $r = 2$ and the number of possible permutations or "words" is $\dfrac{6!}{2!} = \dfrac{720}{2} = 360$.

1 PERMUTATIONS

EXAMPLE 1

How many different 4-digit numbers can be made from the digits 1, 3, 5, and 6 if no digit is used more than once?
If a number is formed randomly using those four digits, what is the probability that it is greater than 3,000?

Strategy: Use Key Concepts 1 and 2.

Step 1: Find the number of permutations of 4 digits. Use 4!.
$4! = 4 \times 3 \times 2 \times 1 = 24$, so 24 different numbers are possible.

Step 2: Find the number of numbers greater than 3,000.
Use the Counting Principle.

First digit	**Second digit**	**Third digit**	**Fourth digit**
3 choices	× 3 choices	× 2 choices	× 1 choice

$3 \times 3 \times 2 \times 1 = 18$, so there are 18 numbers greater than 3,000.
(Note that there are only 3 choices for the first digit. The digit 1 cannot be placed first because the number will not be greater than 3,000.)

Step 3: Find the probability that a number is greater than 3,000.
Use the probability rule $P(E) = \dfrac{\text{favorable outcomes}}{\text{total outcomes}}$.
$P(\text{a number greater than } 3{,}000) = \dfrac{18}{24} = \dfrac{3}{4}$.

Solution: There are 24 possible 4-digit numbers that can be made using the digits 1, 3, 5, and 6. The probability that a number using those digits will be greater than 3,000 is $\dfrac{3}{4}$.

EXAMPLE 2

From a class of 20 students, in how many different ways can a President and Vice-President be selected?

Strategy: Use Key Concept 3.

Step 1: Use the formula $_nP_r = \dfrac{n!}{(n-r)!}$ where $n = 20$ and $r = 2$.

$$\dfrac{20!}{(20-2)!} = \dfrac{20!}{18!} = \dfrac{20 \times 19 \times \cancel{18} \times \cancel{17} \times \cancel{16} \times \ldots \times \cancel{1}}{\cancel{18} \times \cancel{17} \times \cancel{16} \times \ldots \times \cancel{1}}$$

$$= 20 \times 19 = 380$$

Solution: From a class of 20 students, a President and Vice-President can be chosen 380 ways.

EXAMPLE 3

How many different 6-digit numbers can be written using all of the following digits: 2, 5, 5, 6, 6, 6?

Strategy: **Use Key Concept 4.**

Step 1: Use the formula for permutations with repetitions: $\frac{n!}{r!}$ where $n = 2$ (two 5s are used) and $r = 3$ (three 6s are used).

$$\frac{6!}{2!\,(3!)} = \frac{6 \times 5 \times \cancel{4}^{2} \times \cancel{3} \times \cancel{2} \times \cancel{1}}{(\cancel{2} \times 1) \times (\cancel{3} \times \cancel{2} \times \cancel{1})} = 60$$

Solution: **It is possible to make 60 different numbers using all 6 digits.**

REGENTS MATH PRACTICE

1. In how many ways can 4 friends line up for a photograph?

2. How many different 5-letter "words" can be formed from the letters A, C, D, E, H if each letter is used only once per "word"?

3. Find the value of each of the following expressions.
   a. 1!   b. 7!   c. $\frac{10!}{9!}$ d. $\frac{6!}{6!}$

4. In how many different ways can runners finish first, second, and third if there are 8 runners in a race?

5. a. How many different 5-digit numbers can be made from the digits 1, 2, 4, 5, and 8 if each digit is used only once?

   b. How many of the numbers will be greater than 5,000?

   c. If a number is formed randomly what is the probability that it is *less than* 5,000?

6. How many different sets of 2-letter initials can be made from the English alphabet if each pair consists of two different letters?

7. Five students want to sit in the first row of the classroom. If there are only 4 seats, in how many ways is it possible to fill the row?

8. In how many different ways can 4 identical blue shirts and 6 identical green shirts be arranged on a rack in a clothing store if all shirts are displayed?

9. How many different 6-letter "words" can be made from the letters R, A, E, L, R, and C?

10. How many different ways can the letters of the word balloon be arranged?

LESSON 51
COMBINATIONS

KEY CONCEPTS YOU'LL NEED IN THIS LESSON

1. A **combination** is a **set** of objects in which their order is not important. This is different from a permutation, which is an arrangement of objects, in which the order is important.

2. To find a number of combinations of n items, taken r at a time, use the formula:

   $$_nC_r = \frac{_nP_r}{r!}$$ where $_nP_r$ is the number of permutations of the objects.

   - How many different combinations of 3 books can be selected from a shelf holding 8 books?
     Since the order in which the books are chosen is not important, you need to find a number of combinations.

     Use the formula $_nC_r = \frac{_nP_r}{r!}$ where $n = 8$ and $r = 3$

     $$_8C_3 = \frac{_8P_3}{3!} = \frac{8 \times 7 \times 6}{3 \times 2 \times 1} = \frac{336}{6} = 56 \text{ ways}$$ So, 3 books can be chosen from a shelf of 8 books in 56 different ways.

3. Combinations can be used to find probabilities.

   - In the above problem, all the books are presidential biographies and all are identical in size. What is the probability of choosing books about Washington, Adams, and Monroe?
     Use the probability formula and the combination formula.

     $$P(\text{Event}) = \frac{\text{number of favorable outcomes}}{\text{total number of outcomes}}$$

     Number of favorable outcomes = 1 since the 3 books can be chosen in any order .

     Total number of outcomes = 56 since there are 56 ways 3 books can be chosen from 8.

     $$P(\text{choosing Washington, Adams, Monroe}) = \frac{1}{56}$$

1 COMBINATIONS

EXAMPLE 1

Find the value of $_7C_4$.

Strategy: **Use Key Concepts 1 and 2.**

Step 1: Find the number of ways 4 objects can be chosen from 7 objects without regard to order.
Use the combination formula.

$$_nC_r = \frac{_nP_r}{r!}$$

$$_7C_4 = \frac{_7P_4}{4!} = \frac{7 \times 6 \times 5 \times 4}{4 \times 3 \times 2 \times 1} = \frac{840}{24} = 35$$

Solution: **The number of ways 4 objects can be chosen from 7 objects is 35.**

EXAMPLE 2

How many different telephone calls must be made for 10 friends to each speak to one another?

Strategy: **Same as above.**

Step 1: Order does not matter. Since friend A calling friend B is the same as B calling A, this is a problem in combinations.
Use the combinations formula

$$_nC_r = \frac{_nP_r}{r!} \quad \text{where } n = 10 \text{ and } r = 2$$

$$_{10}C_2 = \frac{_{10}P_2}{2!} = \frac{10 \times 9}{2 \times 1} = \frac{90}{2} = 45$$

Solution: **For 10 friends to each speak to one another, 45 phone calls must be made.**

EXAMPLE 3

What is the probability that, if all the friends are together the next day, the first call you will hear about is the one between Arnold and Carla (or any other one particular call)?

Strategy: **Use Key Concept 3.**

Step 1: Find the total number of calls made.
The total is 45.

Step 2: Use the probability formula: $P(\text{Event}) = \dfrac{\text{number of favorable outcomes}}{\text{total number of outcomes}}$

$P(\text{hearing about Arnold and Carla's call}) = \dfrac{1}{45}$

Solution: **The probability that you will hear about a particular call is $\dfrac{1}{45}$.**

REGENTS MATH PRACTICE

In problems 1–6, find the value of the expression.

1. $_6C_6$

2. $_8C_1$

3. $_{12}C_2$

4. $_9C_0$

5. $_7C_6$

6. $_{10}C_4$

7. How many different combinations of 4 shirts can you pack for a trip if you have 15 shirts in your closet?

8. From a class of 24 seniors, in how many different ways can 2 students be chosen to represent the class at a school meeting?

9. From the class described in problem 8, how many different ways can two students be elected class president and class vice president?

10. Explain the different results for problems 8 and 9.

11. From a box of 20 different colored pencils, what is the probability that you will pick red and orange pencils?

12. From your class of 23 students, 3 are selected at random to go on a trip, what is the probability that you and your two closest friends will be the ones selected?

Notice: Photocopying any part of this book is forbidden by law.

221

UNIT 9 REVIEW

1. The data represent the number of runs scored by major league baseball teams during one week of play.

   6, 7, 1, 0, 0, 3, 7, 8, 2, 4, 4, 1, 2, 4, 5, 2, 7, 8, 4, 3, 8, 0, 4, 1, 5, 10, 7, 6, 2, 11, 4, 3, 2

   a. Complete a frequency table.
   b. How many times did teams score more than 8 runs?
   c. What was the mode number of runs scored?
   d. To the nearest tenth, what was the mean number of runs scored by the teams?

2. Use the data from problem 1 to complete the frequency table below.

Runs Scored	Frequency
0–2	
3–5	
6–8	
9–11	

3. For the data in problem 2, name the modal interval or intervals.

4. To the nearest tenth, what percent of the time did a team score more than 2 runs?

5. Use the data from problem 1 to complete the cumulative frequency table below.

Runs Scored	Cumulative Frequency
0–11	
0–8	
0–5	
0–2	

6. For the baseball data, which interval is the 50th percentile or median?

7. The probability of successfully completing a difficult mountain climb without an accident is $\frac{1}{15}$.

What is the probability that there will be some kind of accident if you attempt the climb?

8. A fast-food restaurant menu lists 9 different types of burgers, 3 sizes of fries, and 8 different drinks. If you have one from each list, how many different meals are possible?

9. If you eat at the restaurant described in problem 8 and have a small order of fries every day, what is the probability that your meal will contain a giant burger and a chocolate shake?

10. A test consists of 10 multiple-choice questions, each with 4 possible answers. If you know the answers to 5 of the questions and guess on the other 5, what is the probability that your grade will be 100%?

11. If two cards are drawn from a standard deck of 52 playing cards without replacement, what is the probability that the first is red and the second is the 7 of clubs?

12. How many different ways can the digits 5, 7, 9, and 2 be arranged to form the last 4 digits of a telephone number?

13. What is the probability that if the digits in problem 12 are arranged randomly, the telephone number will end with two odd digits?

14. How many different ways can the letters of the word HAPPINESS be arranged?

15. From a gym class of 32 students, 5 are selected randomly to represent the class in a tournament. What is the probability that the students selected are Ann, Charles, Ed, Gloria, and Ilene?

LESSON 52
OPEN SENTENCES, CLOSED SENTENCES, NEGATIONS

KEY CONCEPTS YOU'LL NEED IN THIS LESSON

1. A mathematical sentence with a variable is an **open sentence**. You cannot tell whether an open sentence is true or false unless you know the value of the variable.

2. A mathematical sentence whose truth value can be determined is a **closed sentence** or a **statement**.

3. A statement has one of two truth values: either True or False, never both.

4. When you know the truth value of a statement, you can tell the truth value of its **negation**. A statement and its negation always have opposite truth values.

5. The symbol for negation is ~.

    If p is: There are 24 hours in a day,
    then $\sim p$, its negation, is: There are not 24 hours in a day.

    For any statement p, the following truth table always applies:

p	$\sim p$
T	F
F	T

6. If there is more than one negation symbol, work inside parentheses first, as you would with the order of operations.

---

1 OPEN AND CLOSED SENTENCES

EXAMPLE 1

Which of the following is an open sentence?
a. Toyota is a manufacturer of cars.
b. Baseball is played during the spring.
c. The new millennium begins this year.
d. There are five quarters in one dollar.

Strategy: Use Key Concepts 1, 2, and 3.

Step 1: Examine each sentence to determine whether you can tell the truth value.
a. Toyota is a manufacturer of cars. (The sentence is true.)
b. Baseball is played during the spring (The sentence is true.)

---

c. The new millennium begins this year. (You cannot tell the truth value without knowing the year. The sentence is open.)

d. There are five quarters in one dollar. (The sentence is false.)

Solution: **Only sentence c is open.**

---

2 NEGATION

EXAMPLE 2

Write the negation of the sentence: Every leap year is not a Presidential election year.

Strategy: **Use Key Concepts 4 and 5.**

Step 1: Think of the sentence, Every leap year is not a Presidential election year, as *p*. Then the negation is ~*p*.

Step 2: Write ~*p* as an English sentence, making its truth value the opposite of the original sentence: Every leap year is a Presidential election year.

Solution: **The negation of *Every leap year is not a Presidential election year* is *Every leap year is a Presidential election year*.**

EXAMPLE 3

Consider the statement *t*: Every other year, there is a Congressional election. What is the meaning of ~(~*t*)?

Strategy: **Use Key Concepts 4, 5, and 6.**

Step 1: Write the meaning of ~*t*:
Every other year, there is not a Congressional election.

Step 2: Write the negation of ~*t*:
Every other year, there is a Congressional election.

Solution: **~(~*t*) means the same as *t*. The two negations cancel each other out.**

REGENTS MATH PRACTICE

In 1–3, choose the open sentence.

1. a. $7 + 3 = 12$
    b. $16 \div 2 = 8$
    c. $3(6) = 18$
    d. $y - 3 = 15$

2. a. An airplane flies.
    b. A car travels on a road.
    c. That car is very fast.
    d. A snail crawls at a snail's pace.

3. a. He does his homework every night.
    b. Studying is a sure way to help your grades.
    c. Tests are important.
    d. Good attendance can help you with your schoolwork.

4. Let p be: The picture is not hanging evenly on the wall. Write the negation of p in symbols and in words.

5. Let s be: The plant is too large for the room. Write the negation of s in symbols and in words.

6. Let q be: The room does not have one window on each wall. Write the negation of q in symbols and in words.

7. Let r be: The house has seven rooms. Write the meaning of the following symbols as an English sentence: $\sim(\sim r)$.

8. If p is: The square of 9 is 79, which of the following is $\sim p$?
    a. The square of 9 is 81.
    b. The square of 9 is 3.
    c. The square of 9 is not 79.
    d. The square of 9 is not 3.

9. If p is: $x + 2 < 9$, which of the following values of x makes p a false statement?
    a. 7   b. 6   c. 5   d. 4

10. If q is: $x - 5 > 3$, which of the following values makes $\sim(\sim q)$ a true statement?
    a. 9   b. 8   c. 7   d. 6

LESSON 53
CONJUNCTIONS AND DISJUNCTIONS

KEY CONCEPTS YOU'LL NEED IN THIS LESSON

1. A **conjunction** is a compound sentence formed by joining two simple sentences with the word "and."

    Consider the following two propositions:
    p: I got a hit. q: We won the game.

    The conjunction is: I got a hit and we won the game.
    The symbol for conjunction is: $\wedge$
    The symbol for the conjunction of p and q is $p \wedge q$.

    The truth table for the conjunction $p \wedge q$ is

p	q	$p \wedge q$
T	T	T
T	F	F
F	T	F
F	F	F

    For a conjunction to be true, **both** p and q must be true.

2. A **disjunction** is a compound sentence formed by joining two simple sentences with the word "or."

    Consider the following two propositions:
    p: I will work on Saturday. q: I will go to the park.

    The disjunction is: I will work on Saturday or I will go to the park.
    The symbol for disjunction is: $\vee$
    The symbol for the disjunction of p and q is $p \vee q$.

    The truth table for the disjunction $p \vee q$ is

p	q	$p \vee q$
T	T	T
T	F	T
F	T	T
F	F	F

    For a disjunction to be true, **either** part may be true or the **whole** statement may be true.

1 CONJUNCTION

EXAMPLE 1

Use the following sentences:
k: The car trip is very long.
l: I am tired.
m: I will travel tomorrow.

Write using symbols:
a: The car trip is very long and I am tired.
b: I am tired and I will not travel tomorrow.

Strategy:	**Use Key Concept 1.**
a. Step 1:	Write the symbolic form for *The car trip is very long.* (*k*)
Step 2:	Write the symbolic form for *I am tired.* (*l*)
Solution :	**The conjunction *The car trip is very long and I am tired* is *k* ∧ *l*.**
b: Step 3:	Write the the symbolic form for the sentence *I am tired.* (*l*)
Step 4:	Think of the positive form of the sentence *I will not travel tomorrow.* (*m*)
Step 5:	Write the negation of *m*. (~*m*)
Solution:	**The conjunction *I am tired and I will not travel tomorrow* is *l* ∧ ~*m*.**

2 DISJUNCTION

EXAMPLE 2

Use the sentences from Example 1. Write in symbolic form: *The car trip is not very long or I am tired.*

Strategy:	**Use Key Concept 2.**
Step 1:	Write the negation of the statement *The car trip is very long.* (~*k*)
Step 2:	Write the statement *I am tired* in symbolic form. (*l*)
Solution:	**The disjunction *The car trip is not very long or I am tired* is ~*k* ∨ *l*.**

3 DETERMINING THE TRUTH OF A STATEMENT

EXAMPLE 3

Each of the following statements is true.
p: Every triangle is a polygon.
q: Every polygon has more than two sides.

Write the meaning of each statement below given in symbolic form.
Then determine whether the statement is true or false.
a: $p \lor \sim q$ b: $\sim p \land q$

Strategy: **Use Key Concepts 1 and 2.**

a. Step 1: Write the compound statement:
Every triangle is a polygon or every polygon does not have more
than two sides.

Step 2: Determine the truth value of each part.
Every triangle is a polygon. (T)
Every polygon does not have more than two sides. (F)

Step 3: Use the second row of the truth table for disjunction from Key
Concept 2: T F T.

Solution: **Since one part of the disjunction is true, the entire statement**
is true.

b. Step 1: Write the compound statement:
Every triangle is not a polygon and every polygon has more than
two sides.

Step 2: Determine the truth value of each part.
Every triangle is not a polygon. (F)
Every polygon has more than two sides. (T)

Step 3: Use the third row of the truth table for conjunction from Key
Concept 1: F T F

Solution: **Since only one part of the conjunction is true, the statement**
is false.

4 **COMPLETING A TRUTH TABLE**

EXAMPLE 4

Complete this truth table.

1	2	3	4	5	6	7
p	q	$\sim p$	$\sim q$	$p \wedge \sim q$	$p \vee q$	$(p \wedge \sim q) \wedge (p \vee q)$

Strategy: **Use Key Concepts 1 and 2.**

Step 1: Fill in columns 1 and 2, using all possible combinations of p and q.

Step 2: Fill in columns 3 and 4, using the negations of columns 1 and 2.

Step 3: Fill in column 5, a conjunction, using the truth values from columns 1 and 4.
Notice that only row 2 is true.

Step 4: Fill in column 6, a disjunction, using the truth values from columns 1 and 2.
Notice that only row 4 is false.

Step 5: Fill in column 7, another conjunction, using truth values from columns 5 and 6.
Only row 2 is true, since only in row 2 are both columns 5 and 6 true.

Solution: **The completed truth table is shown below:**

1	2	3	4	5	6	7
p	q	$\sim p$	$\sim q$	$p \wedge \sim q$	$p \vee q$	$(p \wedge \sim q) \wedge (p \vee q)$
T	T	F	F	F	T	F
T	F	F	T	T	T	T
F	T	T	F	F	T	F
F	F	T	T	F	F	F

REGENTS MATH PRACTICE

In Exercises 1–5, use the following sentences:

   m: The Mediterranean is an ocean.
   p: The Pacific is an ocean.
   d: An ocean is deep.

Write each sentence in symbolic form. Then write whether the sentence is true or false.

1. The Mediterranean and the Pacific are oceans.

2. The Mediterranean is not an ocean or an ocean is deep.

3. The Mediterranean is an ocean, or the Pacific is an ocean and an ocean is deep.

4. The Mediterranean or the Pacific are oceans, and an ocean is not deep.

5. It is not true that the Pacific is not an ocean, and an ocean is deep.

In Exercises 6–8, the truth values of the first two sentences are given. Determine the truth value of the third sentence.

6. I do my homework. (True)
    I listen to music. (False)
    I do my homework or I listen to music.

7. I don't listen to music or I don't watch TV (False)
    I don't listen to music. (False)
    I don't watch TV.

8. The plant gets enough sun or the plant dies. (True)
    The plant does not get enough sun. (True)
    The plant dies.

In Exercises 9 and 10, complete the truth table.

9.

p	*q*	*p* ∨ *q*	~*q*	(*p* ∨ *q*) ∧ ~*q*
T	T			
T	F			
F	T			
F	F			

10.

p	*q*	*p* ∧ *q*	~*p*	~*q*	~*p* ∨ ~*q*	(*p* ∧ *q*) ∨ (~*p* ∨ ~*q*)

LESSON 54
CONDITIONALS, BICONDITIONALS, TAUTOLOGIES

KEY CONCEPTS YOU'LL NEED IN THIS LESSON

1. A **conditional** is a compound sentence formed by joining two simple sentences with the words "if...then."

   p: I need orange juice.　　q: I will go shopping.
   premise　　　　　　　　　conclusion

   The conditional is: If I need orange juice, then I will go shopping.
   The symbol for the conditional is →.
   "If p, then q" is written $p \rightarrow q$.

   The truth table for the conditional is

p	q	$p \rightarrow q$
T	T	T
T	F	F
F	T	T
F	F	T

   Notice that the conditional is false only when a true premise leads to a false conclusion.

2. A **biconditional** is a compound sentence formed by a conjunction as follows:
   $p \rightarrow q$ (if p then q) AND $q \rightarrow p$ (if q then p)

   The biconditional can be written $(p \rightarrow q) \wedge (q \rightarrow p)$, but it is usually shortened to $p \leftrightarrow q$ and is read as "p if and only if q."

   The truth table for the biconditional is

p	q	$p \leftrightarrow q$
T	T	T
T	F	F
F	T	F
F	F	T

   Notice that the biconditional is true when p and q have the **same truth values**: either both true or both false.

3. A **tautology** is a compound sentence that is always true. A tautology can be seen in a truth table.

   p: I am a student. q: I study for tests.

p	q	$p \wedge q$	$(p \wedge q) \rightarrow p$
T	T	T	T
T	F	F	T
F	T	F	T
F	F	F	T

The statement "If I am a student and I study for tests, then I am a student," is always true, regardless of the truth values of p and q. Therefore, $(p \wedge q) \rightarrow p$ is a tautology.

1 CONDITIONALS

EXAMPLE 1

Use the following sentences:
t: Trees bloom in the spring. (True)
f: Flowers bloom in the cold. (False)
v: Vegetables grow in warm weather. (True)

Write each sentence below using symbols. Then determine whether the sentence is true or false.
a: If trees bloom in spring, then flowers bloom in the cold.
b: If vegetables do not grow in warm weather, then flowers do not bloom in the cold.

Strategy: **Use Key Concept 1.**

a. Step 1: Write the symbolic form: $t \rightarrow f$

Step 2: Write the truth value of each part: True $\rightarrow$ False

Solution: **True $\rightarrow$ False is a false conditional.**

b. Step 1: Write the symbolic form: $\sim v \rightarrow \sim f$

Step 2: Write the truth value of each part: False $\rightarrow$ True

Solution: **False $\rightarrow$ True is a true conditional.**

2 BICONDITIONALS

EXAMPLE 2

Use the following sentences:
r: A triangle is a right triangle.
t: a triangle has a 90° angle.

Determine the truth value of the biconditional:
A triangle is not a right triangle if and only if it does not have a 90° angle.

Strategy: **Use Key Concept 2.**

Step 1: Write the necessary column headings in the truth table.

r	t	~r	~t	~r ↔ ~t
T	T	F	F	T
T	F	F	T	F
F	T	T	F	F
F	F	T	T	T

Step 2: Interpret the last column.
When sentences r and t are either both true or both false, the biconditional is true.

Solution: **The statement $\sim r \leftrightarrow \sim t$ is true when both r and t are true or when both r and t are false.**

---

③ TAUTOLOGIES

EXAMPLE 3

Use the following sentences:
p: I pay \$5 for a game.
s: I save money.
$p \rightarrow s$: If I pay \$5 for a game, then I save money.

Combine the sentences to form "If I pay \$5 for a game then I save money, and I pay \$5."

Do I save money?

Strategy: **Use Key Concept 3.**

p	s	p → s	(p → s) ∧ p	((p → s) ∧ p) → s
T	T	T	T	T
T	F	F	F	T
F	T	T	F	T
F	F	T	F	T

Solution: **Since the last column is always true, it is a tautology.**
Therefore, I do save money.

REGENTS MATH PRACTICE

Use the following sentences for questions 1–4.

> *h*: Elephants are heavy. (True)
> *f*: Elephants can fly.　(False)

1. Which statement or statements are true?
    a. $h \wedge f$
    b. $h \vee f$
    c. $h \rightarrow f$
    d. $h \leftrightarrow f$

2. Which of the following statements are true?
    f. $h \rightarrow \sim f$
    g. $\sim h \rightarrow f$
    h. $\sim h \rightarrow \sim f$
    j. $h \wedge \sim f$

3. When $h \rightarrow f$ is false, which is true?
    a. *h* is true and *f* is true.
    b. *h* is false and *f* is true.
    c. *h* is false and *f* is false.
    d. *h* is true and *f* is false.

4. Which sentence means the same as $f \leftrightarrow \sim h$?
    f. Elephants can fly if and only if they are not heavy.
    g. If elephants can fly, then they are not heavy.
    h. If elephants cannot fly, they are heavy.
    j. Elephants can fly if and only if they are heavy.

Use the following sentences for questions 5–8.

> *t*: Today is Tuesday.
> *w*: Tomorrow is Wednesday.
> *m*: Yesterday was Monday.

Write each statement in symbolic form.

5. Tomorrow is Wednesday if and only if yesterday was Monday.

6. Today is not Tuesday if and only if tomorrow is not Wednesday.

7. Yesterday was Monday if and only if today is Tuesday.

8. Yesterday was not Monday if and only if today is not Tuesday.

In questions 9 and 10, complete the truth tables. Then decide whether the statement in the last column is a tautology.

9.

p	q	p → q	p ∧ (p → q)	(p ∧ (p → q)) → p

10.

p	q	~q	p → ~q	p ∧ q	~(p ∧ q)	p → ~q ↔ ~(p ∧ q)

LESSON 55
INVERSE, CONVERSE, CONTRAPOSITIVE

KEY CONCEPTS YOU'LL NEED IN THIS LESSON

1. **Inverse:** To form the inverse of a conditional, negate both the premise and the conclusion.

   The truth table for the inverse is:

				Conditional	Inverse
p	q	$\sim p$	$\sim q$	$p \rightarrow q$	$\sim p \rightarrow \sim q$
T	T	F	F	T	T
T	F	F	T	F	T
F	T	T	F	T	F
F	F	T	T	T	T

2. **Converse:** To form the **converse** of a conditional, flip the premise and the conclusion.

   The truth table for the converse is:

		Conditional	Converse
p	q	$p \rightarrow q$	$q \rightarrow p$
T	T	T	T
T	F	F	T
F	T	T	F
F	F	T	T

3. **Contrapositive:** To form the **contrapositive** of a conditional, negate both parts **and** flip them.

   The truth table for the contrapositive is:

				Conditional	Contrapositive
p	q	$\sim q$	$\sim p$	$p \rightarrow q$	$\sim q \rightarrow \sim p$
T	T	F	F	T	T
T	F	T	F	F	F
F	T	F	T	T	T
F	F	T	T	T	T

SUMMARY

p	q	Conditional $p \rightarrow q$	Inverse $\sim p \rightarrow \sim q$	Converse $q \rightarrow p$	Contrapositive $\sim q \rightarrow \sim p$
T	T	T	T	T	T
T	F	F	T	T	F
F	T	T	F	F	T
F	F	T	T	T	T

Notice the following:

A conditional and its inverse do not always have the same truth values. They are **not logically equivalent.**

A conditional and its converse are **not logically equivalent.** However, the inverse and converse of the same conditional are logically equivalent.

A conditional and its contrapositive **always have the same truth values.** They are **logically equivalent.**

1 INVERSE, CONVERSE, CONTRAPOSITIVE

EXAMPLE 1

Use the statements:
p: I did not eat lunch. (True)
q: I am hungry before dinner. (False)

a. **Write the English translation of $p \rightarrow q$. Give its truth value.**
b. **Write the inverse, converse, and contrapositive of the conditional. Give the truth value of each.**

Strategy: **Use Key Concepts 1, 2, and 3.**

a. **Step 1:** Write the English translation:
If I did not eat lunch, then I am hungry before dinner.

Step 2: Find the truth values in the truth table for the conditional.

p	q	$p \rightarrow q$
T	T	T
T	F	F
F	T	T
F	F	T

A true premise leading to a false conclusion is a false conditional.

Solution: **The conditional $p \rightarrow q$ is false.**

b. Step 1: Write the inverse: $\sim p \rightarrow \sim q$
If I did eat lunch, then I am not hungry before dinner.

Step 2: Write the truth values of each part of the inverse.
Since p is true, $\sim p$ must be false. Since q is false, $\sim q$ must be true.
So, $F \rightarrow T$

Solution: **$F \rightarrow T = T$, so the inverse is true.**

Step 3: Write the converse: $q \rightarrow p$
If I am hungry before dinner, then I did not eat lunch.
Write the truth values of each part of the converse: $F \rightarrow T$

Solution: **$F \rightarrow T = T$, so, the converse is true.**

Step 4: Write the contrapositive: $\sim q \rightarrow \sim p$
If I am not hungry before dinner, then I did eat lunch.
Write the truth values of each part of the contrapositive: $T \rightarrow F$

Solution: **$T \rightarrow F = F$, so, the contrapositive is false.**

REGENTS MATH PRACTICE

In questions 1–4, write the symbolic form of the given sentence, give the English translation, and give its truth value.

Use the statements:
m: Time marches on. (True)
t: Tomorrow follows today. (True)
y: Yesterday follows tomorrow. (False)

1. The inverse of $m \rightarrow t$

2. The converse of $m \rightarrow t$

3. The contrapositive of $m \rightarrow t$

4. The converse of $y \rightarrow t$

5. Write the contrapositive in English of "If a quadrilateral has exactly one pair of parallel sides, it is a trapezoid."

6. Write the converse in English of "If you do not eat well, you do not exercise."

7. Write the inverse in English of "If the Knicks lost, they scored fewer than 90 points."

In questions 8–10, the conditional statement is true.

8. "If you live in Buffalo, you go to school in New York State."

   Write the converse of the statement. Is the converse true, false, or is it impossible to tell?

9. If $x + 3 = 12$, then $2x = 18$.

   Write the inverse of the statement. Is the inverse true, false, or is it impossible to tell?

10. If you are on the Internet, then you are not watching television.

    Write the contrapositive of the statement. Is the contrapositive true, false, or is it impossible to tell?

LESSON 56
LOGICAL EQUIVALENCE

KEY CONCEPTS YOU'LL NEED IN THIS LESSON

1. When two statements always have the same truth values, they are **logically equivalent**.

2. You can determine whether statements are logically equivalent by building a truth table.

3. The conditional $p \rightarrow q$ and its contrapositive $\sim q \rightarrow \sim p$ are logically equivalent.

4. For the conditional $p \rightarrow q$, its inverse $\sim p \rightarrow \sim q$, and its converse $q \rightarrow p$ are logically equivalent.

---

1 LOGICAL EQUIVALENCE

EXAMPLE 1

a. Complete the truth table.

p	q	$\sim q$	$p \rightarrow q$	$\sim (p \rightarrow q)$	$p \wedge \sim q$
T	T	F	T		F
T	F	T	F		T
F	T	F	T		F
F	F	T	T		F

b. If p is "I walk to school" and q is "I take the bus," which of the following statements is logically equivalent to $\sim (p \rightarrow q)$?

1. **If I do not walk to school, then I do not take the bus.**
2. **I do not walk to school, and I take the bus.**
3. **I walk to school, and I do not take the bus.**
4. **I do not walk to school, and I do not take the bus.**

Strategy: **Use Key Concepts 1, 2, 3, and 4.**

Step 1: Examine the truth table for the truth values of $\sim (p \rightarrow q)$. The statement is true only in the second row of the table, where p is true and q is false.

Step 2: Write each of the four choices in symbolic form.
1. If I do not walk to school, then I do not take the bus. $\sim p \rightarrow \sim q$
2. I do not walk to school, and I take the bus. $\sim p \wedge q$
3. I walk to school, and I do not take the bus. $p \wedge \sim q$
4. I do not walk to school, and I do not take the bus. $\sim p \wedge \sim q$

Notice: Photocopying any part of this book is forbidden by law.

Step 3: Determine which statement is represented in the truth table.
$p \wedge \sim q$ is in the table.

Step 4: Compare the truth values of $p \wedge \sim q$ and $\sim(p \rightarrow q)$. Since they are always the same, the two statements are logically equivalent.

Solution: **"I walk to school and I do not take the bus" is logically equivalent to "It's not true that if I walk to school, I take the bus."**

REGENTS MATH PRACTICE

In questions 1–3, the first statement is true. Choose the statement that must also be true.

1. If a figure is a regular polygon, then all sides of the figure are congruent.

   a. If all sides of a figure are congruent, then the figure is a regular polygon.
   b. If a figure is not a regular polygon, then all sides are not congruent.
   c. If all sides of a figure are not congruent, then the figure is not a regular polygon.
   d. If all sides of a figure are not congruent, then the figure is a regular polygon.

2. If you may vote in an election, you are at least 18 years old.

   f. If you may not vote in an election, you are not at least 18 years old.
   g. If you are at least 18 years old, you may vote in an election.
   h. If you are at least 18 years old, you may not vote in an election.
   j. If you are not at least 18 years old, you may not vote in an election.

3. If it is snowing, it is not summer.

   a. If it is summer, it is not snowing.
   b. If it is not summer, it is snowing.
   c. If it is summer, it is snowing.
   d. If it is not snowing, it is summer.

4. Which statement is logically equivalent to $\sim p \to q$?
   f. $p \to \sim q$
   g. $\sim p < -- > q$
   h. $q \to \sim p$
   j. $\sim q \to p$

5. Which statement is logically equivalent to $\sim q \to \sim p$?
   a. $\sim p \to q$
   b. $p \to \sim q$
   c. $q \to p$
   d. $p \to q$

6. Which statement is the contrapositive of $q \to p$?
   f. $p \to q$
   g. $\sim p \to \sim q$
   h. $\sim p \to q$
   j. $\sim q \to \sim p$

7. Which statement is logically equivalent to $\sim (p \to q)$?
   a. $p \to q$
   b. $p \vee \sim q$
   c. $p \wedge \sim q$
   d. $\sim q \to p$

8. In question 7, p is "Today is Monday," and q is "I am going to school." Which statement is logically equivalent to "It is not true that if today is Monday then I am going to school"?

   f. If today is Monday, then I am going to school.
   g. Today is Monday or I am not going to school.
   h. Today is Monday and I am not going to school.
   j. It is not true that if I am going to school today, then it is Monday.

9. Which statement is logically equivalent to $\sim (p \wedge q)$?
   a. $\sim p \to \sim q$
   b. $q \to \sim p$
   c. $p \to q$
   d. $q \to p$

10. In question 9, p is "I work," and q is "I earn money." Which statement is logically equivalent to "If I earn money, then I do not work"?

    f. If I do not work, then I do not earn money.
    g. I work and I earn money.
    h. If I earn money, then I work.
    j. It is not true that I work and I earn money.

LESSON 57
DRAWING CONCLUSIONS

KEY CONCEPTS YOU'LL NEED IN THIS LESSON

1. If a conjunction is true, both of its statements must be true.

2. If a disjunction is true, at least one of its statement must be true. Therefore, if one statement is false, the other must be true.

3. You can determine whether conclusions can be drawn from a conditional by analyzing the truth values of the statements making up the conditional.

1 CONJUNCTIONS

EXAMPLE 1

What conclusions can be drawn from the following true conjunction?
The weather is warm, and I go swimming.

Strategy: **Use Key Concept 1.**

Step 1: Write the two statements that make up the conjunction in English and in symbolic form.
p: The weather is warm.
q: I go swimming.
$p \wedge q$: The weather is warm, and I go swimming.

Step 2: Analyze the symbolic form.
For $p \wedge q$ to be true, both p and q must be true.

Solution: **The conclusions that can be drawn are:**
The weather is warm.
I go swimming.

2 DISJUNCTIONS

EXAMPLE 2

What conclusion can be drawn from the following true statements?
I clean my room, or I don't go to the mall.
I don't clean my room.

Strategy:	**Use Key Concept 2.**
Step 1:	Write the two statements that make up the disjunction in English and in symbolic form. *p*: I clean my room. *q*: I don't go to the mall. *p* ∨ *q*: I clean my room, or I don't go to the mall. ~ *p*: I don't clean my room.
Step 2:	Analyze the symbolic form. *p* ∨ *q* is true and ~ *p* is true. So, *p* must be false and *q* must be true.
Solution:	**The conclusion that can be drawn is: I don't go to the mall.**

3 CONDITIONALS

EXAMPLE 3

What conclusion can be drawn from the following true statements?
If I do not write with ink, I can erase.
I cannot erase.

Strategy:	**Use Key Concept 3.**
Step 1:	Write the sentences symbolically along with their truth values. ~ *p* → *q*: If I do not write with ink, I can erase. (True) ~ *q*: I cannot erase. (True)
Step 2:	Analyze the symbolic forms. Since ~ *q* is true, *q* must be false. In order to make ~ *p* → *q* true, ~ *p* must also be false. So, *p* must be true.
Solution:	**Since *p* is true, the conclusion that can be drawn is *p*, I do write with ink.**

EXAMPLE 4

What conclusion can be drawn from the following true statements?
If the light is out, the room is dark.
The light is not out.

Strategy:	**Use Key Concept 3.**
Step 1:	Write the sentences symbolically along with their truth values. p: The light is out. q: The room is dark. $p \rightarrow q$: If the light is out, the room is dark. (True) $\sim p$: The light is not out. (True)
Step 2:	Analyze the symbolic forms. Since $\sim p$ is true, p must be false. Since p is false and $p \rightarrow q$ is true, q can be either true or false.
Solution:	**No conclusion can be drawn.**

REGENTS MATH PRACTICE

In each question, the first two sentences are true. Decide whether the third sentence is true or false, or whether you cannot tell.

1. I run fast or I do not win the race.
    I win the race.
    I run fast.

2. If today is Friday, then the weekend begins today.
    Today is not Friday.
    The weekend begins today.

3. If I live in New York, I do not root for the New York Yankees.
    I root for the New York Yankees.
    I live in New York.

4. $p \rightarrow q$
    $\sim p$
    $\sim q$

5. $\sim p \vee q$
    $\sim q$
    $\sim p$

6. $\sim p \vee \sim q$
    p
    q

7. $\sim p \wedge \sim q$
    p
    q

8. $\sim q \rightarrow \sim p$
    p
    q

9. x is a perfect square if and only if x has a rational number square root.

    x does not have a rational number square root.

    x is not a perfect square.

10. If the angle measures 123°, the angle is an obtuse angle.

    The angle does not measure 123°.

    The angle is an obtuse angle.

LESSON 58
REASONING WITH DIAGRAMS

KEY CONCEPTS YOU'LL NEED IN THIS LESSON

1. Venn diagrams are often used to show the relationship between sets. The overlapping part of the diagram shows that objects are members of both sets.

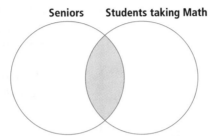

Seniors   Students taking Math

The overlapping section of the diagram represents seniors who are studying math.

1   REASONING WITH DIAGRAMS

EXAMPLE 1

There are 34 students taking biology and 13 students taking biology and earth science. A total of 50 students are taking either biology or earth science or both. How many students are taking only biology? Only earth science?

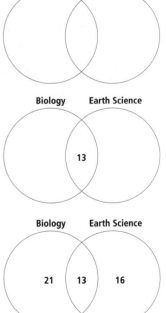

Strategy: **Use Key Concept 1.**

Step 1: Draw the Venn diagram and label each section.

Step 2: Place the number that you know in the diagram. You know that 13 students are studying both subjects. So, place 13 in the overlapping section.

Step 3: Complete the Venn diagram.
Since 34 students are studying biology, there must be 34 – 13 or 21 students who are studying **only** biology.
Since a total of 50 students are taking one or the other or both subjects, there must be 50 – 34 or 16 students who are studying **only** earth science.

Solution: **21 students are studying only biology, and 16 students are studying only earth science.**

REGENTS MATH PRACTICE

In one class of 32 students, 17 like orange juice, 19 like grape juice, and 12 like both.

1. How many students like only orange juice?

2. How many students like only grape juice?

3. How many students like neither orange or grape juice?

4. There are 41 band members and 6 students who are members of the band and a sports team. There are 102 students who are either in the band, on a team, or take part in both activities. How many students are only on a sports team?

Of 29 students in a class, 8 had been to Europe and 3 had been to Europe and Asia. A total of 10 students had traveled to one of the two continents.

5. How many students had been only to Asia?

6. How many students had not been to either Europe or Asia?

On a baseball team, 22 players bat right-handed, 7 bat left-handed, and 4 can bat either left- or right-handed.

7. How many players bat only left-handed?

8. How many players bat only right-handed?

9. How many players are on the team?

10. Mike's Pizzeria sold 105 pies on Saturday. He used sausage on 65 of them, pepperoni on 52, and both sausage and pepperoni on 12. How many pies had only pepperoni?

UNIT ⑩ REVIEW

1. Let *p* represent: *m* − 5 > 6. Which value or values make *p* a false statement?
   a. 10   b. 11
   c. 12   d. 13

2. Let *q* represent: A picture is worth a thousand words. What is the meaning of ∼ (∼ *q*)?

In questions 3–5, use the following true statements.

Let *t* represent: Talk is cheap.
Let *l* represent: Actions speak louder than words.
Write each statement in symbolic form. Then write whether the statement is true or false.

3. Talk is cheap or actions do not speak louder than words.

4. Talk is not cheap and actions speak louder than words.

5. Talk is not cheap if and only if actions do not speak louder than words.

In questions 6 and 7, use the following statements:

Let *b* represent: You are in Boston.
Let *n* represent: You are in New England.

6. Write the converse in English of the statement *b* → *n*. Must the conditional and its converse have the same truth values?

7. Write the contrapositive in English of *b* → *n*. Must the conditional and its contrapositive have the same truth values?

8. Which statement must have the same truth values as: If you are in Chicago, then you are not in New England?

   a. In you are in New England, then you are in Chicago.
   b. If you are not in Chicago, then you are not in New England.
   c. If you are in Chicago, then you are in New England.
   d. If you are in New England, then you are not in Chicago.

9. The first two statements are true. Is the third statement true, false, or is it impossible to tell?
   ∼ *p* ∧ ∼ *q*
   ∼ *q*
   p

10. A clothing store has 25 blue shirts and 11 blue shirts with a stripe. There are 42 shirts that are either blue, striped, or blue with a stripe. How many shirts are striped, but not blue?

The best test-taking tip anyone can ever be given, of course, is: "**Learn the math!**"

All the other tips are useless if you neglect this one.

There are, however, many additional things that you can do to improve your test-taking ability. Here are several.

1 TIPS THAT RELATE TO ANSWERING MULTIPLE-CHOICE QUESTIONS

- It's best to try to solve the problem before looking at the answer choices. But, if you can't solve the problem and must guess, **eliminate obviously incorrect choices** before you guess.

  Example: Michael has completed $\frac{5}{6}$ of his homework. About what percent has he completed?

  a. 5.6%   b. 33%   c. 56%   d. 83%

When you think of the fraction $\frac{5}{6}$ you know that it represents most of the entire amount. In this problem, you can eliminate 5.6% since it represents only a small part out of 100%. You can also eliminate 33% since you know that it is about $\frac{1}{3}$. So, if you have to guess, you can guess between 2 choices, not 4. The correct answer is d. 83%.

- If you need to do computation, see whether you can **simplify the amount of computation** that you actually have to do.

  Example: A football field is 120 yd long by 53 yd wide. What is its area?

  a. 173 yd²   b. 346 yd²   c. 6,360 yd²   d. 6,363 yd²

Once you realize that the answer has to be either choice c. or d., you can quickly see that you only need to multiply the ones places. The product of 3 and 0 is 0, so the digit in the ones place of the product must be 0. The correct answer choice is c. 6,360 yd².

- **Use the work-backwards strategy.** You know that the answer is there on the page. In some problems, you can try each answer to see whether it solves the problem.

  Example: A toll road charges $0.50 for all trips plus $0.05 for each mile. If your toll is $2.75, how many miles did you travel?

  a. 40   b. 45   c. 50   d. 55

You can solve this problem with an equation. But, you can also try each answer choice until you find the one that makes the total cost equal to $2.75.

a. If you traveled 40 miles, the cost would be $0.50 + 40($0.05) or $2.50.

b. If you traveled 45 miles, the cost would be $0.50 + 45($0.05) or $2.75.

So, the solution to the problem must be choice b. 45.

2 TIPS THAT RELATE TO ALL TYPES OF QUESTIONS

- **Use a diagram to help you get a feel for the answer.** In many problem that include diagrams, you can get an idea of the size of the answer required by studying the diagram.

Example:

How long is side *BC* in parallelogram *ABCD* if the perimeter of the figure is 158 cm?

a. 26 cm　　　　　b. 53 cm　　　　　c. 79 cm　　　　　d. 106 cm

26 cm is not correct. Even though the diagram may not be drawn exactly to scale, you know that *BC* is not about 4 times as long as *AB*. So, answer choice d. 106 cm is not correct.

The answer must be either b. 53 cm or c. 79 cm. You can then use what you know about perimeter to find that the correct answer must be choice b. 53 cm.

- **Substitute simple numbers for variables** to help understand the problem.

Example:　Angela grew 3 inches over the summer. If *b* was her height before the summer and *a* was her height after the summer, which equation would you use to find her height before the summer?

a. $a + 3 = b$　　b. $b - a = 3$　　c. $a = b - 3$　　d. $a - 3 = b$

To solve a problem like this, you can substitute easy numbers and see which choice makes sense. Say that Angela was 47 inches before the summer and 50 inches after the summer. So, $b = 47$ and $a = 50$.

a. $a + 3 = b \rightarrow 50 + 3 \neq 47$ so choice a. is not correct.
b. $b - a = 3 \rightarrow 47 - 50 \neq 3$ so choice b. is not correct.
c. $a = b - 3 \rightarrow 50 \neq 47 - 3$ so choice c. is not correct
d. $a - 3 = b \rightarrow 50 - 3 = 47$ is the only choice that makes sense, so the correct answer is choice d.

- **Be sure that you have solved the whole problem**, not just a part of it. You can do this if you read the problem carefully and ask yourself "What am I being asked to find?"

  Example: A playground is made up of 3 triangular sections. In each section, the length of the base of the triangle is 60 ft and the length of the height is 40 ft. What is the area of the playground?

  If you remember the formula for the area of a triangle, $A = \frac{1}{2} \times b \times h$, you can solve this problem easily.

  $$\text{Area} = \frac{1}{2} \times 60 \times 40 = \frac{1}{2} \times 2{,}400 = 1{,}200$$

  But 1,200 is the area of just one of the triangles. It is not the solution to this problem!

  Read carefully—and you'll find that the problem asks for the area of the entire playground.

  So, you must multiply the area of one section by 3. The area of the playground is $3 \times 1{,}200$ or $3{,}600$ ft².

AND FINALLY, maybe the most important thing you can do on any test:

- After you think you have solved a problem, always ask yourself:

  Does my answer make sense?

The test consists of 4 parts. In each part, answer all questions. The value of the questions in each part are given at the beginning of each section.

Part I
Each correct answer is worth 2 points.

1. A family has 4 children. What is the probability that there are no boys in the family?

    1) $\frac{1}{4}$ 　　　　2) $\frac{1}{8}$ 　　　　3) $\frac{1}{16}$ 　　　　4) $\frac{15}{16}$

2. Which is the contrapositive of "If opposite sides of a quadrilateral are congruent, then the quadrilateral is a parallelogram"?

    1) If opposite sides of a quadrilateral are not congruent, then the quadrilateral is not a parallelogram.

    2) If a quadrilateral is not a parallelogram, then opposite sides are not congruent.

    3) If opposite sides of a quadrilateral are congruent, then the quadrilateral is not a parallelogram.

    4) If a quadrilateral is a parallelogram, then opposite sides are not congruent.

3. What are the coordinates of the image of (-2, 7) after a reflection about the *y*-axis?

    1) (-2, -7) 　　　2) (2, -7) 　　　　3) (7, -2) 　　　　4) (2, 7)

4. Find the difference: $(-5x^2 + 3x - 1) - (2x^2 + 4)$

    1) $-7x^2 + 3x - 5$ 　　2) $-3x^2 + 3x - 3$ 　　3) $7x^2 + 3x - 5$ 　　4) $-3x^2 - 3x - 5$

5. Which could not be the sides of a triangle?

    1) 6.5, 9.2, 13 　　2) $\frac{1}{2}, \frac{2}{3}, \frac{3}{4}$ 　　　3) 3, 6, 9 　　　　4) 4.5, $3\frac{1}{2}$, 7.5

6. Find the sum: $\frac{1}{x} + \frac{1}{x-2}$ where $x \neq 0$ and $x \neq 2$

    1) $\frac{2x-2}{x^2-2x}$ 　　2) $\frac{2x-1}{x^2}$ 　　　3) $\frac{x^2}{x^2-2x}$ 　　　4) $\frac{x}{x^2-2}$

7. How many different ways can a 4-member committee be chosen from a class of 20 students?

    1) 116,280 　　　2) 29,070 　　　3) 4,845 　　　　4) 80

8. What is the solution set of the equation $x^2 + 2x - 15 = 0$?

   1) {-3, -5}   2) {-5, 3}   3) {3, 5}   4) {-3, 5}

9. What is the percent reduction if a $25 book is selling for $18?

   1) 7%   2) 18%   3) 28%   4) 72%

10. Which is equivalent to 2^8?

    1) $4^3 \cdot 2^2$ 2) $2^4 \cdot 2^2$ 3) $8^2 \times 2^3$ 4) 8^2

11. In isosceles triangle ABC, the exterior angle at base angle C is 130°. What is the measure of vertex angle B?

    1) 40°   2) 50°   3) 80°   4) 100°

12. Robert, Chan, and Doris are all saving for new in-line skates. Chan has saved four times the amount Robert has saved. Doris has three times as much as Robert. If they have a total of $288 between them, how much has Doris saved?

    1) $36   2) $72   3) $96   4) $108

13. What is the circumference of a circle whose area is 49π?

    1) 7π 2) 14π 3) $\dfrac{14}{\pi}$ 4) $\dfrac{7}{\pi}$

14. A school librarian orders new novels and non-fiction books in the ratio 9 to 5. If he orders 315 new novels, how many non-fiction books will he order?

    1) 7   2) 45   3) 63   4) 175

15. If $\sqrt{n} < n < n^2$, which could be n?

    1) $\dfrac{1}{4}$ 2) $\dfrac{1}{2}$ 3) 1   4) 2

16. What is the slope of the line whose equation is $3x - 2y = 5$?

    1) $\dfrac{-2}{3}$ 2) $\dfrac{2}{3}$ 3) $\dfrac{3}{2}$ 4) $\dfrac{-3}{2}$

17. Of 35 dishes served by a restaurant, 22 contain garlic, 16 contain onions, and 7 contain both garlic and onions. How many dishes contain neither garlic or onions?

    1) 4   2) 6   3) 9   4) 13

18. Which is equivalent to the expression $18\sqrt{48}$?

    1) $54\sqrt{3}$ 2) $36\sqrt{3}$ 3) 72   4) $72\sqrt{3}$

19. A cube has a volume of 64 cm³. If the edge of the cube is tripled in length, what will be the volume of the resulting cube?

    1) 144 cm³   2) 192 cm³   3) 576 cm³   4) 1,728 cm³

20. What must be the value of x so that the mean, median, and mode of the set will all have the same value?

    1, 4, 6, 6, 7, 8, x

    1) 9   2) 10   3) 11   4) 12

Part II
Show all your work, including steps taken, as well as diagrams, graphs, drawings, or formulas used. Each correct answer is worth 2 points.

21. Complete the quadrilateral so that it has exactly 2 lines of symmetry.

22. A formula for the distance required for a car to stop on dry pavement is $d = 1.1s + 0.05s^2$ where d is the required distance needed to stop in feet and s is the speed in miles per hour.

    a) Find the distance needed to stop a car traveling at 30 miles per hour.

    b) A car traveling at highway speed requires 260 feet to stop. To the nearest mile per hour, find the speed of the car.

23. a)   For which of the following can an exact value be determined?

    area of a circle,   volume of a sphere,   volume of a cylinder,   volume of a pyramid

    b)   Explain why no exact value can be found for the other measures.

24. Find the quotient: $\dfrac{4m^2 + 6mn}{5m + 9mn} \div \dfrac{8m^2 - 10mn}{18mn + 10m}$

25. The cost of a taxi ride is \$2.00 for the first $\frac{1}{5}$ mile and \$0.30 for each additional $\frac{1}{5}$ mile. At night, there is \$0.50 surcharge added to the cost of a ride. If Elizabeth got into a taxi at 9:05 PM and paid a total of \$7.60, how far did she ride?

Part III

Show all your work, including steps taken, as well as diagrams, graphs, drawings, or formulas used. Each correct answer is worth 3 points.

26. The graph shows the distances covered by two bicycle racers, A and B.

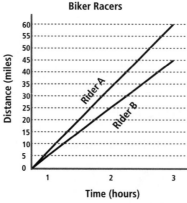

a)   How much faster, in miles per hour, is rider A traveling than rider B?

b)   If they kept riding at the same pace, after a total of how many hours of riding would they be 22.5 miles apart?

27. A storage locker in the shape of a rectangular prism has a volume of 27 ft³. A company wants to store cartons that are 18 in. long, 12 in. wide, and 9 in. high. How many cartons will have the same volume as the locker?

28. Each day for 7 days, Hope plans to put some money away. She wants to have at least \$15 saved by the end of the week. If she increases the amount she puts away each day by \$0.50 over the previous day, what is the least amount she must put away the first day, to the nearest cent?

29. A family drove an average of 192 miles per day over a 5-day trip. On one day, they drove 230 miles, on another 187 miles. On each of the other 3 days, they drove the same number of miles. How far did they drive on each of those days?

30. In the figure, *ABDF* is a square, *OBCD* is a semicircle, and *DEF* is a right triangle. Find the area of the entire figure, expressed in terms of π.

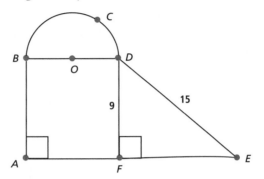

Part IV

Show all your work, including steps taken, as well as diagrams, graphs, drawings, or formulas used. Each correct answer is worth 4 points.

31. An internet company offers a choice of two plans.

   Plan 1: $3 per month and $0.25 per minute   or
   Plan 2: $20 per month for unlimited use

   The graph of Plan 1 has been drawn on the axes below.

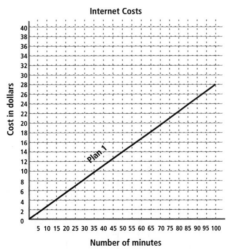

   a) On the same set of axes, draw a graph to represent the cost of plan 2.

   b) For how many minutes of monthly use is it to your advantage to choose plan 2. Explain your answer.

   c) How much do you save by using the less expensive plan if you are on the internet one hour during a month?

32. A group of 6 boys and 4 girls in gym class are choosing a team of 2 players.

    a) What is the probability that both members of the team will be boys?

    b) What is the probability that one team member will be a boy and one will be a girl?

33. A builder wants to construct a ramp from the sidewalk to a doorway. He wants to make the angle at which the ramp climbs as close to 12° as possible. To the nearest foot, how long should the ramp be if the doorway is 6 feet above the sidewalk?

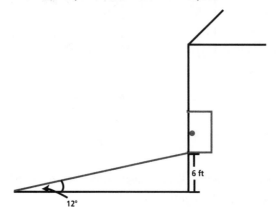

34. Solve the following system of equations for x and y algebraically or graphically.
$$y = x^2 - 2x + 3$$
$$y = x + 1$$

Solve algebraically here.

Solve graphically here.

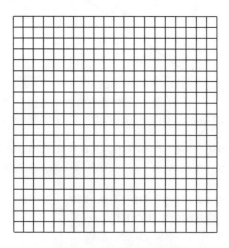

35. The figure represents a picture in a frame. The frame is a circle with diameter 14 in. The picture is a square with side equal to the radius of the circle.

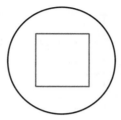

a) Write an algebraic expression that can be used to find the area of the frame.

b) Find the area of the frame to the nearest square inch. Use 3.14 as π.

c) The artist wants the areas of the frame and picture to be as close as possible. To the nearest tenth of an inch, how long should the side of the square be so that the area of the frame will be as close as possible to the area of the picture?

Notice: Photocopying any part of this book is forbidden by law.

259

Conversion Table From Raw Score to Actual Score

Raw Score	Actual Score	Raw Score	Actual Score	Raw Score	Actual Score	Raw Score	Actual Score
85	100	62	83	39	61	16	35
84	99	61	82	38	60	15	34
83	99	60	81	37	59	14	33
82	99	59	80	36	58	13	32
81	99	58	79	35	56	12	31
80	99	57	78	34	55	11	30
79	98	56	78	33	54	10	29
78	97	55	77	32	53	9	28
77	96	54	76	31	52	8	27
76	95	53	75	30	51	7	26
75	94	52	74	29	49	6	25
74	94	51	73	28	48	5	24
73	93	50	72	27	47	4	23
72	92	49	71	26	46	3	22
71	91	48	70	25	45	2	21
70	90	47	69	24	44	1	10
69	89	46	68	23	43	0	0
68	88	45	67	22	42		
67	87	44	66	21	40		
66	87	43	65	20	39		
65	86	42	64	19	38		
64	85	41	63	18	37		
63	84	40	62	17	36		